Theme Reader

Mc Graw Hill **Wright Group**

www.WrightGroup.com

 **Wright Group**

Send all inquiries to:
Wright Group/McGraw-Hill
P.O. Box 812960
Chicago, IL 60681

ISBN 978-0-07-656837-6
MHID 0-07-656837-7

5 6 7 8 9 QVR/LEH 16 15 14 13 12

The McGraw-Hill Companies

Contents

Changes

How do the changes around us make us who we are?

p. 6

Growing and Changing   *Nonfiction: Informational Text*

p. 8

Scaredy Squirrel   *Fiction: Fantasy*

p. 37

THEME
Question

How do the changes around us make us who we are?

Focus Questions

How do things change?

What do we do when things change?

What changes can we choose to make?

How do we change as we grow?

Growing and Changing

by Zoe Smith

Contents

Chapter 1

Changes Ahead

Change happens all the time. It happens to everything and everyone all over the world. Sometimes we **choose** changes, such as when we make new friends. Other changes just happen, such as when we grow taller.

A change can be small or big. Maybe you outgrow your sneakers. This is a small change.

This boy is saying good-bye to his older brother, who is going away to college.

There might be a change in your family. An older brother or sister might leave home to go to college. This is a big kind of change.

Changes at Home

Many things can change at home. Maybe your dad or mom gets a new job. Then he or she isn't at home as often as before. You might need to help out a little more and take on more **responsibilities** to keep things running smoothly.

These boys are helping their family by doing the dishes.

puppy

Alfonso has always wanted to have a dog. This year he got a puppy. Getting a new pet is a fun kind of change.

When your family is expecting a new baby, you might notice some changes around your home.

Maybe you find out that you're going to have a new baby brother or sister. This event is a big change. Your family will be busy getting ready for the new baby. You can help out too!

What other kinds of changes can happen at home?

Changes in Your Neighborhood

Things can change in your neighborhood too. Maybe a new supermarket is built, which makes the streets busier. Then new roads are built to make your neighborhood safer. People might work together to improve a park or playground.

A new playground is a great place to have fun in your neighborhood.

Moving means you have to find your way around a new neighborhood.

Sometimes the buildings in your neighborhood change. An old building might be knocked down. Workers might start building new apartments or a community center. Perhaps you'll move to a new neighborhood, and everything will be new to you.

What other kinds of changes can happen in your neighborhood?

Changes at School

Sometimes changes happen at school. A new gym might be built. Sometimes there are new rules to follow. When a student is new to your class, you might be asked to help him or her. You could even get a new teacher.

Starting third grade is a change too. When you start a new grade, you meet new classmates and make new friends. In a new grade you also start learning new and interesting things.

What other kinds of changes can happen at school?

Chapter 2

Feelings about Change

Changes at Home

Change can happen at any time. One day when you get home from school, you might be told that your grandmother is coming to stay in your room, and you'll share a room with your brother.

You might like spending time with your grandmother.

Have you ever had a new baby brother or sister? Mom and Dad must spend a lot of time taking care of the baby. Maybe you felt a little unhappy that they weren't spending time with you. But when the baby got older and smiled and laughed at you, it made you feel happy. You realized that having a younger brother or sister to play with would be fun.

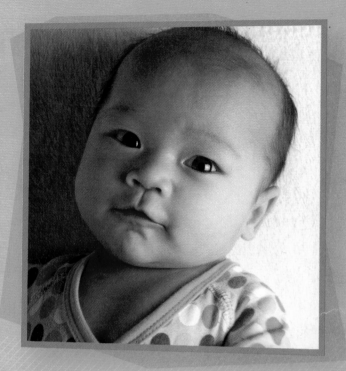

Remember Alfonso and his puppy? He is excited to have a pet, but he is also worried because he doesn't know much about dogs. He decides to go to the library and check out some books on raising a puppy.

Think of some changes that have happened in your home. How did they make you feel?

Changes in Your Neighborhood

boxes

Things can change in your neighborhood. A friend who lives next door might move to a different part of town. You don't want your friend to leave, and it's hard to say good-bye. But you know that you will still be friends—wherever you live.

It's sad when a friend moves away, but it's fun to keep in touch.

A new family might move in next door. There are new children to get to know and new games to play. You might help them unpack their things.

Think of some changes that have happened in your neighborhood. How did they make you feel?

Changes at School

Have you ever started going to a new school? Did you feel **confused** because you weren't sure of where things were? Did you feel a little lonely at first?

Everyone feels nervous about starting at a new school.

Maybe you felt worried and wondered if your classmates would like you. But this was a chance to make some new friends. You may have really liked your new teacher too. You felt a little excited about the future.

Talking to other students or your teacher can help you feel better about a change.

Think of some changes that have happened at school. How did they make you feel?

Chapter 3

Make It Happen!

You don't have to wait for change to happen to you. You can make it happen yourself. Learn a new sport or try a new food. You might be surprised by how much you like change!

This girl is learning about tennis from a coach.

You've made the **decision** to listen to your gym teacher's advice. You're going to work harder at being healthy. What changes could you make? You might ask Mom or Dad to walk you to school instead of riding in the car. You might start eating more fruits and vegetables. Maybe you could encourage your family to eat healthful foods too.

What are some changes that you could make happen around your home?

Taking Action

You can also make changes happen in your neighborhood. Maybe you notice that there is trash lying around in the park. You might get some friends together to begin cleaning up the trash. When the other neighbors see what you're doing, they may want to join in and help.

This girl saw a sign in her neighborhood:

Make a Difference.
Help out at the Animal Shelter!

We need volunteers to take dogs for walks.

If you can help, call the manager.

The girl wants to help, so she asks her dad to call the manager of the shelter. The manager asks them to come in on Saturday morning at 9:00 A.M. Walking a dog is going to be exciting.

What are some actions that you could take to make a difference around your neighborhood?

Learning from Mistakes

No one likes making mistakes. But you can learn from mistakes. They can help you make a change for the better.

If you've made a mistake, look back and see where you went wrong. Then try things differently the next time around.

toaster

Maybe you didn't do well on your last spelling test. So you decide to make a change. You make a plan to study the words every day. You pay more attention in class. Next time you will do well!

What mistakes have you made that you could learn from?

Not studying for his test was a mistake. Next time this boy will do a better job preparing.

Chapter 4

Changing as We Grow

Some changes happen quickly. Other changes happen slowly over a long time.

Have you ever put on a sweater and found that it doesn't fit anymore? How did that happen? You've grown bigger, and you didn't even know it!

Sometimes changes happen so slowly that we don't notice them happening.

You might go away to summer camp, and when you get home, your hair is longer and your bed seems shorter. You've grown!

Animals grow just like people do. Alfonso doesn't have a puppy anymore. It has grown into a dog.

Alfonso has grown too. He's an inch taller than he was last year.

What changes do you notice that show that you have grown?

Helping as We Grow

As you grow older, things change. Your responsibilities will probably change. You might be given more chores to do at home. Maybe you will be asked to take care of a younger sister or brother or help a neighbor.

Chores to do today:

1. Make the bed.
2. Put the toys away.
3. Give the cat fresh water.
4. Feed my fish.

This boy is helping his neighbor carry the groceries.

When you get more responsibilities, you can do more to help the people and places around you.

Now that you are older, what new things do you do in your neighborhood?

What responsibilities do you have now that you didn't have when you were younger? What kinds of changes are you looking forward to as you grow older?

Learning as We Grow

Think about how things have changed since you started school. Now that you're in third grade, you know much more and can do much more than when you were in second grade.

backpack

This boy plays the piano much better than he did when he started two years ago.

As you practice the things you learn, you'll get better at doing them. Your **skills** will improve. Maybe you've started playing basketball and you're getting better at catching the ball. Or you might be learning to play the piano. Can you remember how the music sounded the first time you tried to play?

Which of your skills have changed since last year?

Sum It Up

Change is always happening. Things change around us, and we change too.

We are always growing, and as we grow, the way we look changes. We are always learning and getting better at what we do. As we grow and learn, we change some more.

Some changes are tiny. Some changes are huge. Some changes can be scary, or they can be challenging. But they can also be exciting and fun.

What changes are happening in your life?

by Mélanie Watt

Scaredy Squirrel

Scaredy Squirrel never leaves his nut tree.

the unknown

He'd rather stay in his safe and **familiar** tree than risk venturing out into the unknown. The unknown can be a scary place for a squirrel.

A few things
Scaredy Squirrel
is afraid of:

tarantulas

poison ivy

green Martians

killer bees

germs

sharks

So he's perfectly happy
to stay right where he is.

Advantages
of never leaving
the nut tree:

- great view

- plenty of nuts

- safe place

- no

Disadvantages of never leaving the nut tree:

- same old view

- same old nuts

- same old place

Monday   Tuesday   Wednesday   Thursday

Friday   Saturday   Sunday

In Scaredy Squirrel's nut tree, every day
is the same. Everything is predictable.
All is under control.

Scaredy Squirrel's daily routine:

 6:45 a.m.	wake up	
 7:00 a.m.	eat a nut	
 7:15 a.m.	look at view	

12:00 noon	eat a nut	
12:30 p.m.	look at view	
5:00 p.m.	eat a nut	
5:31 p.m.	look at view	

8:00 p.m.	go to sleep	

BUT let's say, just for example, that something unexpected DID happen...

You can rest assured that this squirrel is **prepared**.

A few items in Scaredy Squirrel's emergency kit:

parachute

bug spray

mask and rubber gloves

hard hat

antibacterial soap

calamine lotion

net

bandage

sardines

What to do in case of an emergency according to Scaredy Squirrel:

Step 1: Panic

Step 2: Run

Step 3: Get kit

Step 4: Put on kit

Step 5: Consult Exit Plan

Step 6: Exit tree (if there is absolutely, definitely, truly no other option)

Dramatization

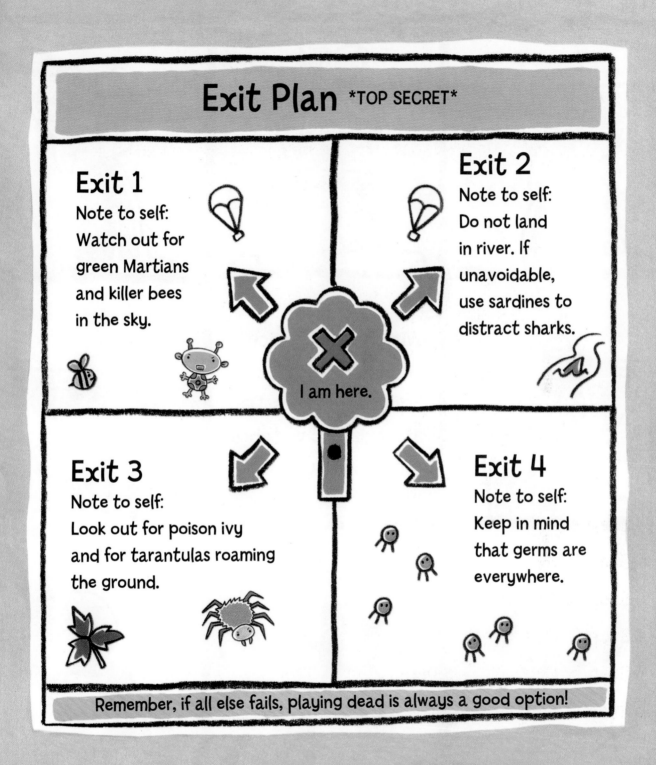

With his emergency kit in hand, Scaredy Squirrel watches. Day after day he watches, until one day...

Thursday
9:37 a.m.

A killer bee appears!

Scaredy Squirrel jumps in panic, knocking his emergency kit out of the tree.

This was NOT part of the Plan.

Scaredy Squirrel jumps to catch his kit.
He quickly regrets this idea.
The parachute is in the kit.

But something incredible happens...

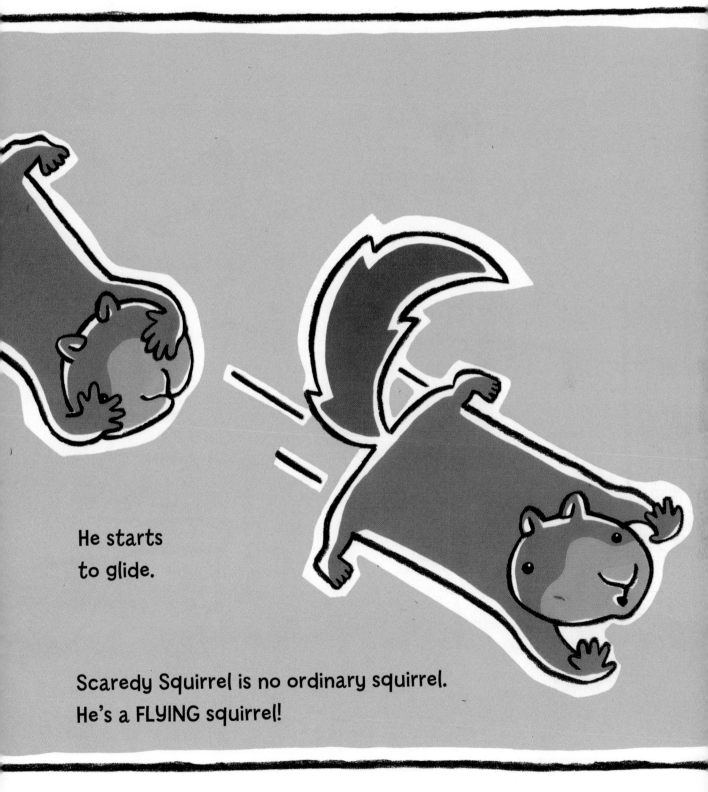

He starts
to glide.

Scaredy Squirrel is no ordinary squirrel.
He's a FLYING squirrel!

He feels overjoyed!

Adventurous!

Scaredy Squirrel forgets all about the killer bee, not to mention the tarantulas, poison ivy, green Martians, germs, and sharks.

Carefree!

Alive!

Until he lands in a bush...

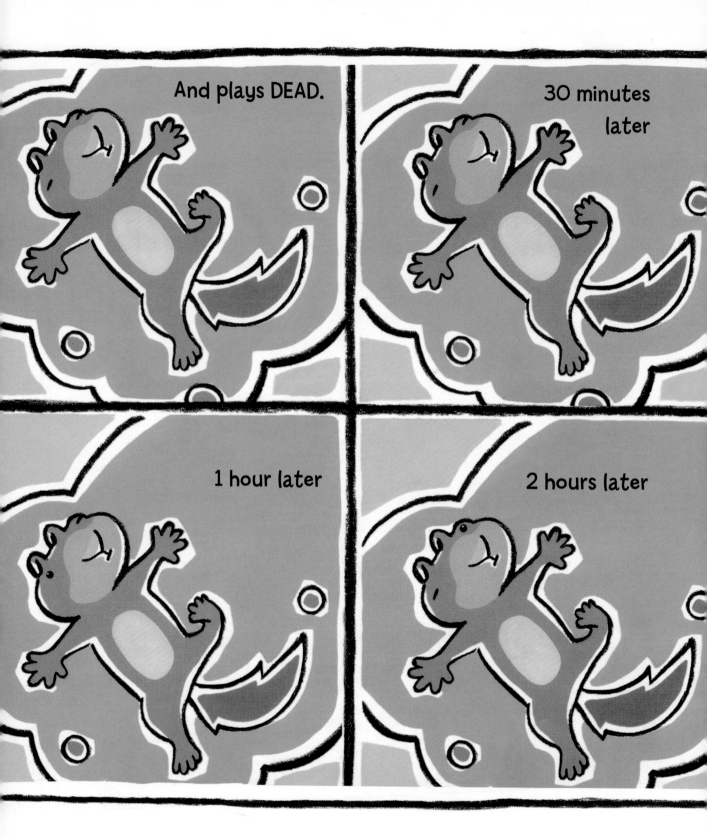

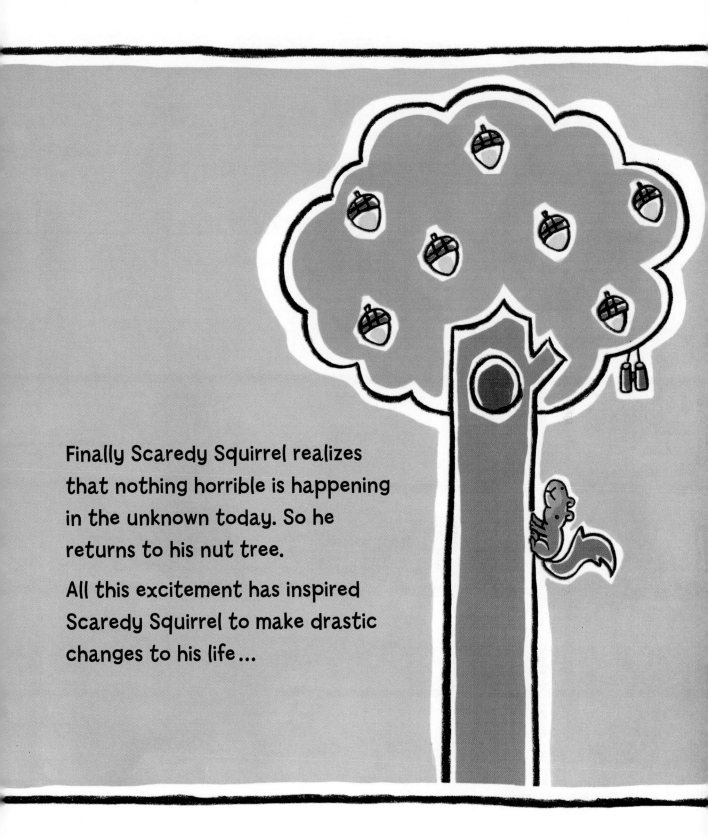

Finally Scaredy Squirrel realizes that nothing horrible is happening in the unknown today. So he returns to his nut tree.

All this excitement has inspired Scaredy Squirrel to make drastic changes to his life...

Scaredy Squirrel's new-and-improved daily routine:

6:45 a.m.	wake up	
7:00 a.m.	eat a nut	
7:15 a.m.	look at view	
9:37 a.m.	jump into the unknown	

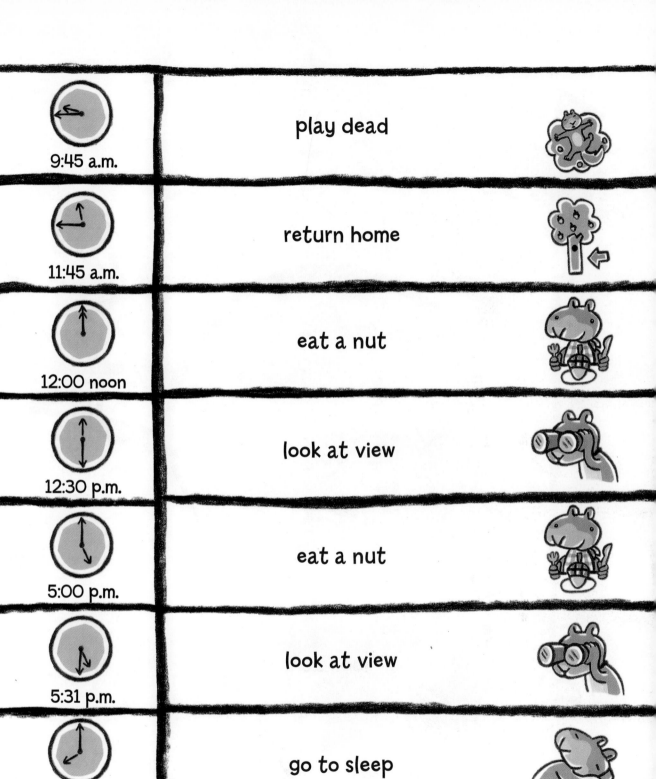

9:45 a.m.	play dead	
11:45 a.m.	return home	
12:00 noon	eat a nut	
12:30 p.m.	look at view	
5:00 p.m.	eat a nut	
5:31 p.m.	look at view	
8:00 p.m.	go to sleep	

poison ivy

P.S. As for the emergency kit, Scaredy Squirrel is in no hurry to pick it up just yet.

Science at Play

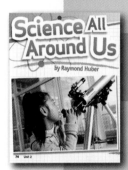
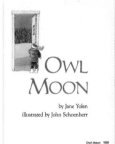

THEME
Question

How does science help us have fun?

Focus Questions

What role does science play in sports?

How does science create new ways to have fun?

How does science help us understand the natural world?

How can we explore the science behind fun activities?

Science All Around Us

by Raymond Huber

Contents

Chapter 1

Bats and Bicycles

"Play ball!" The pitcher throws the ball toward you. You swing the bat. Smack! It's a home run!

Sports are fun. But did you know that fun is all about fascinating **forces**? You can discover the science that makes fun possible in this book.

glove

Bat Power

When you swing a baseball bat and hit the ball, the force from the bat shifts to the ball and makes it move. A force makes an object move, stop, or change direction. You cannot see forces, but you can see how they make things move.

Down to Earth

What makes a baseball come down when it's up in the air? It's gravity—the force that pulls all objects toward Earth. You can test gravity by jumping as high as you can. No matter how high you jump, gravity will pull you down to Earth!

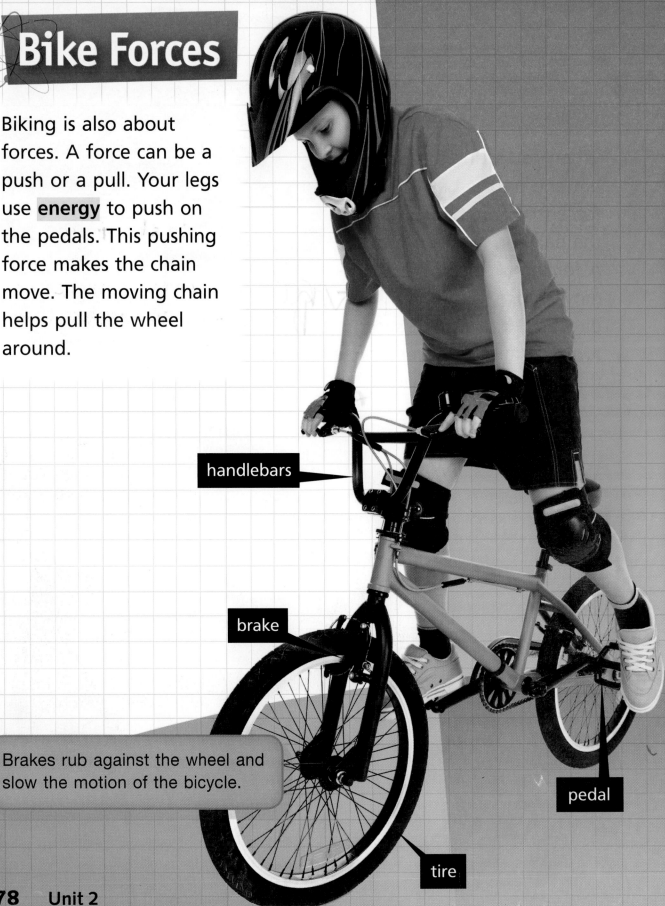

Bike Forces

Biking is also about forces. A force can be a push or a pull. Your legs use **energy** to push on the pedals. This pushing force makes the chain move. The moving chain helps pull the wheel around.

handlebars

brake

Brakes rub against the wheel and slow the motion of the bicycle.

pedal

tire

Other forces slow you when you're on a bike. Friction is a force between two surfaces that rub together. There's friction where the tires touch the road. On a rough road there's more friction, so you need to pedal harder. On a smooth surface there's less friction, so it's easier to ride.

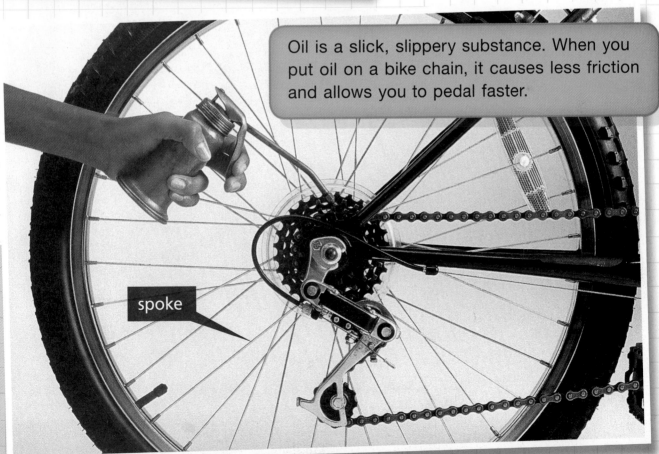

Oil is a slick, slippery substance. When you put oil on a bike chain, it causes less friction and allows you to pedal faster.

spoke

What Is Energy?

You and your friend are racing each other on bikes. Your friend moves faster. Maybe your friend has more energy. Energy is the ability to do work. Your bike will move faster if you push harder on your pedals.

These cyclists are using energy to race on bicycles. Who do you think is using more energy?

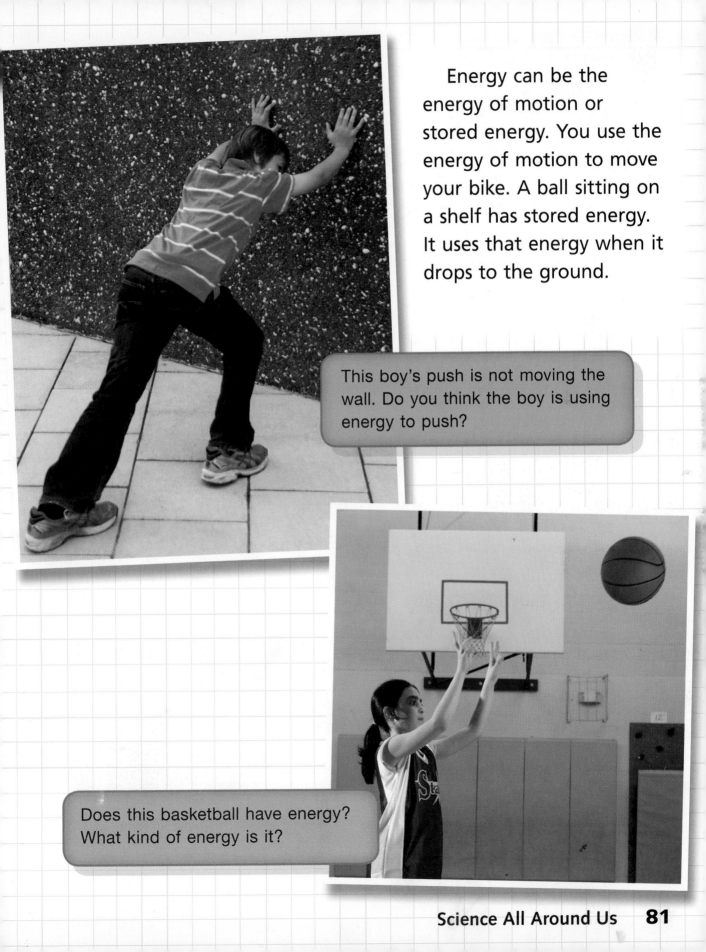

Energy can be the energy of motion or stored energy. You use the energy of motion to move your bike. A ball sitting on a shelf has stored energy. It uses that energy when it drops to the ground.

This boy's push is not moving the wall. Do you think the boy is using energy to push?

Does this basketball have energy? What kind of energy is it?

Chapter 2

Playing with Technology

What else about science affects how things work? Can you imagine how people lived before they had phones, cars, and computers? **Technology** has helped change many lives.

Technology is about using skills and knowledge to make tools, machines, and materials. Technology can also be the materials and machines themselves, such as a computer.

Some classes are taught using computers, not books.

Listen to the Radio

Before TV was invented, listening to the radio was one of the most popular ways of having fun. Every night many families gathered around the radio.

War of the Worlds

Once, in 1938, some listeners forgot that radio stories weren't real. The radio played a story from a book called *The War of the Worlds*. The story was about aliens from Mars landing on Earth. Many people believed the story was real. They called the police or ran away from their homes!

The War of the Worlds was written by the author H. G. Wells.

Moving Images

Another way of having fun was to go to the movies. The very first movies had no sound. The pictures were black and white. Later, new technology allowed moviemakers to add sound and color to their movies.

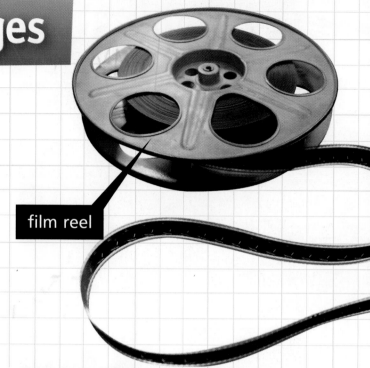

film reel

3-D Movies

Why would you wear a pair of funny glasses at the movies? You might do this to see a 3-D movie! These glasses use simple technology to make a movie look as though it is happening right in front of you. Some objects seem closer than they really are. Others seem to leap out of the screen!

3-D movies became very popular in the 1950s.

television

Exciting new technology became widely available in the 1950s. TV allowed people to see moving pictures and hear sound in their own living rooms. After a short time more people were watching TV than listening to the radio.

In the 1950s watching TV was an exciting event for many families.

Coming to Life

Do you have a favorite cartoon show? Cartoon shows use animation. People who make cartoon shows draw each action that a character does. When the drawings flow past quickly, it seems as if the character is actually moving.

Today people use computers to animate TV shows, movies, and computer games.

Time Line of Inventions

1930s
Movies with color

1950s
First color TVs

1920s
First black-and-white TVs and movies with sound

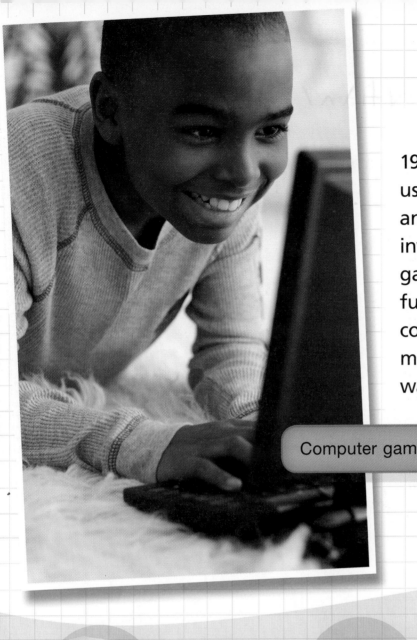

At the end of the 1950s, people began to use computers to make animations. Then people invented the first video games. But the first full-length movie using computer animation wasn't made until 1995. That movie was called *Toy Story*.

Computer games can be a lot of fun.

1970s

Home computers
and home
computer games

1980s

The Internet

1990s

DVD players

2000s

MP3 players

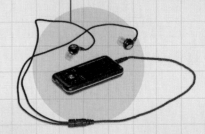

Special Sports

Inventors have created special technology for athletes with disabilities. Amputees—people who have lost a limb or part of a limb—might wear artificial limbs called prostheses.

prosthetic leg

Winning Legs

Rudy Garcia-Tolson is a double amputee. When he was 19 years old, Garcia-Tolson won a gold medal in swimming at the 2008 Paralympics in Beijing, China. He has also completed many triathlons. How does he do this? He has a lot of determination, and he trains regularly with his pair of prostheses! Garcia-Tolson has used sports technology to become a top athlete.

Special wheelchairs have made many sports possible for people with disabilities. People can use wheelchairs fitted with extra wheels to take part in events.

Amputees can use skis with bucket seats. The seat softens the bumps as the skier rushes over the snow. Technology has helped many people to go faster and farther—and to have fun!

This person is skiing using specially designed skis and ski poles.

Chapter 3

Take a Closer Look

You're hiking in the woods. You hear a bird singing. A brightly colored bird flies away quickly. Your field guide lists five birds that sing squeaky songs and fly quickly. Only one is brightly colored. It's the hummingbird. That must be the bird you saw.

You can use binoculars to watch birds.

dog

bear

You can **observe** nature as if you're a scientist. Scientists use their five senses—sight, smell, touch, taste, and hearing—to observe things around them. Then they **classify**, or group, living things based on their qualities. Classifying things helps scientists understand nature better.

cat

Forest World

You continue your hike. Can you see the differences among the plants around you?

Plants come in all shapes and sizes. Scientists look at plants closely to find out how they are different and how they are the same.

This scientist grows plants in a greenhouse to study them more closely.

Some leaves look like they have fingers, while others are a single piece.

Look at the forest floor. Did you know that the forest floor is home to billions of living things? Earthworms and insects may live there. You can study these creatures more closely with a magnifying glass or microscope.

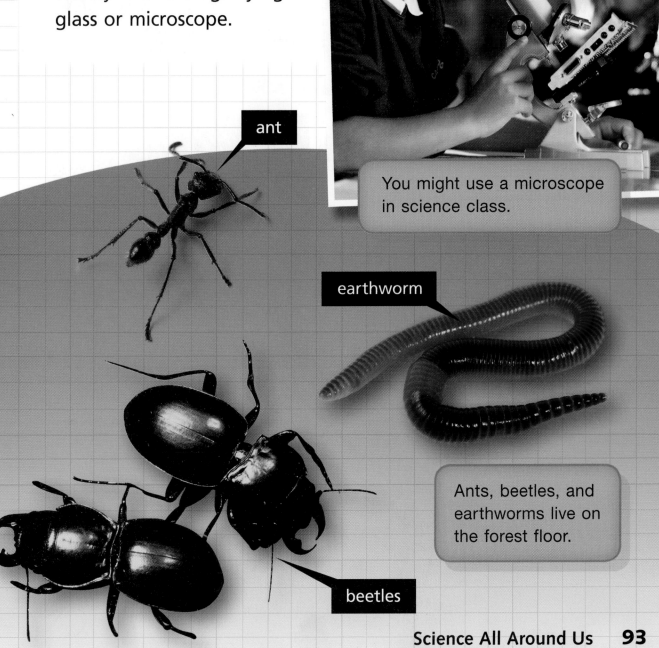

ant

earthworm

beetles

You might use a microscope in science class.

Ants, beetles, and earthworms live on the forest floor.

Look Up

A telescope also lets you look at things more closely. It makes the stars look bigger and closer. You can see more stars through a telescope than by using the naked eye.

Telescopes

This kind of telescope uses glass lenses to collect light and then send the light to a point of focus. The focused light is then sent to the eyepiece.

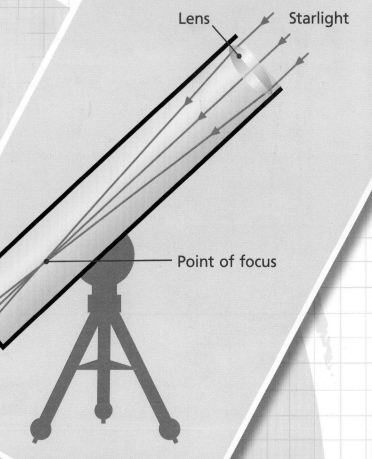

Telescope

Lens

Starlight

Point of focus

Eyepiece

Some telescopes are very powerful. The Hubble Space Telescope explores the sky while it moves around Earth. It uses mirrors to reflect light from things in space onto special cameras. The cameras take pictures. Then computers on the telescope send the pictures back to Earth. The U.S. space program, NASA, makes telescopes that use cutting-edge technologies.

This image of a spiral galaxy was taken using NASA telescopes.

galaxy

Chapter 4

Surprising Science

Playgrounds and Parks

Science is even at work in playgrounds and fun parks.

Imagine you're on a swing. You pump your legs to make the swing move. This movement creates the force that pushes the swing higher. You feel as if you're flying!

The harder you pump your legs, the higher the swing will go.

Sliding

A slide is also fun. It takes energy to climb to the top of a slide. Then you can sit down and slide to the bottom. Gravity helps pull you down. The smooth surface has less friction so you can move faster.

Ferris Wheels

Electricity powers most Ferris wheels. A Ferris wheel takes you high into the sky and then slowly returns you to Earth. The electricity drives a powerful motor that gives the wheel the energy to turn.

Making It Move

The Ferris wheel was first introduced at the World's Columbian Exposition of 1893 in Chicago, Illinois. There, many Americans witnessed electricity for the first time.

bumper

Bumper Cars

Have you ever wondered how people crash bumper cars without being hurt? Bumper cars use energy and force. When one car crashes into another, the rubber bumper spreads out the force of the crash. The riders wear seatbelts to keep safe.

Loop the Loop

A roller coaster does amazing twists and loops. Chains and a small motor pull it up the first hill. After that the roller coaster completes the ride on its own. How does it do it?

a loop

Gravity and momentum keep the roller coaster moving after the first hill. As the roller coaster climbs each hill, there is more distance for gravity to pull it down the other side. A roller coaster has momentum because it is a big object that is moving. Momentum helps the roller coaster climb each hill.

Sum It Up

Next time you ride a bike, gaze at the stars, or ride a roller coaster, think about the science that is at play. Find out about the technology, forces, or energy that make that activity possible!

Science is behind nature and just about everything you do for fun. So how is science at play in your life?

OWL
MOON

by Jane Yolen
illustrated by John Schoenherr

It was late one winter night,
long past my bedtime,
when Pa and I went owling.
There was no wind.
The trees stood still
as giant statues.
And the moon was so bright
the sky seemed to shine.
Somewhere behind us
a train whistle blew,
long and low,
like a sad, sad song.

I could hear it
through the woolen cap
Pa had pulled down
over my ears.
A farm dog answered the train,
and then a second dog
joined in.
They sang out,
trains and dogs,
for a real long time.
And when their voices
faded away
it was as quiet as a dream.
We walked on toward the woods,
Pa and I.

Our feet crunched
over the crisp snow
and little gray footprints
followed us.
Pa made a long **shadow**,
but mine was short and round.
I had to run after him
every now and then
to keep up,
and my short, round shadow
bumped after me.

But I never called out.
If you go owling
you have to be quiet,
that's what Pa always says.

I had been waiting
to go owling with Pa
for a long, long time.

We reached the line
of pine trees,
black and pointy
against the sky,
and Pa held up his hand.
I stopped right where I was
and waited.
He looked up,
as if **searching** the stars,
as if reading a map up there.
The moon made his face
into a silver mask.
Then he called:
"Whoo-whoo-who-who-who-whooooooo,"
the sound of a Great Horned Owl.
"Whoo-whoo-who-who-who-whooooooo."

Again he called out.
And then again.
After each call
he was silent
and for a moment we both listened.
But there was no answer.
Pa shrugged
and I shrugged.
I was not disappointed.
My brothers all said
sometimes there's an owl
and sometimes there isn't.

We walked on.
I could feel the cold,
as if someone's icy hand
was palm-down on my back.
And my nose
and the tops of my cheeks
felt cold and hot
at the same time.
But I never said a word.
If you go owling
you have to be quiet
and make your own heat.

We went into the woods.
The shadows
were the blackest things
I had ever seen.
They stained the white snow.
My mouth felt furry,
for the scarf over it
was wet and warm.
I didn't ask
what kinds of things
hide behind black trees
in the middle of the night.
When you go owling
you have to be brave.

Then we came to a clearing
in the dark woods.
The moon was high above us.
It seemed to fit
exactly
over the center of the clearing
and the snow below it
was whiter than the milk
in a cereal bowl.

I sighed
and Pa held up his hand
at the sound.
I put my mittens
over the scarf
over my mouth
and listened hard.
And then Pa called:
"*Whoo-whoo-who-who-who-whooooooo.*
Whoo-whoo-who-who-who-whooooooo."
I listened
and looked so hard
my ears hurt
and my eyes got cloudy
with the cold.
Pa raised his face
to call out again,
but before he could
open his mouth
an echo
came threading its way
through the trees.
"*Whoo-whoo-who-who-who-whooooooo.*"

Pa almost smiled.
Then he called back:
"*Whoo-whoo-who-who-who-whooooooo,*"
just as if he
and the owl
were talking about supper
or about the woods
or the moon
or the cold.
I took my mitten
off the scarf
off my mouth,
and I almost smiled, too.

The owl's call came closer,
from high up in the trees
on the edge of the meadow.
Nothing in the meadow moved.
All of a sudden
an owl shadow,
part of the big tree shadow,
lifted off
and flew right over us.
We watched silently
with heat in our mouths,
the heat of all those words
we had not spoken.
The shadow hooted again.

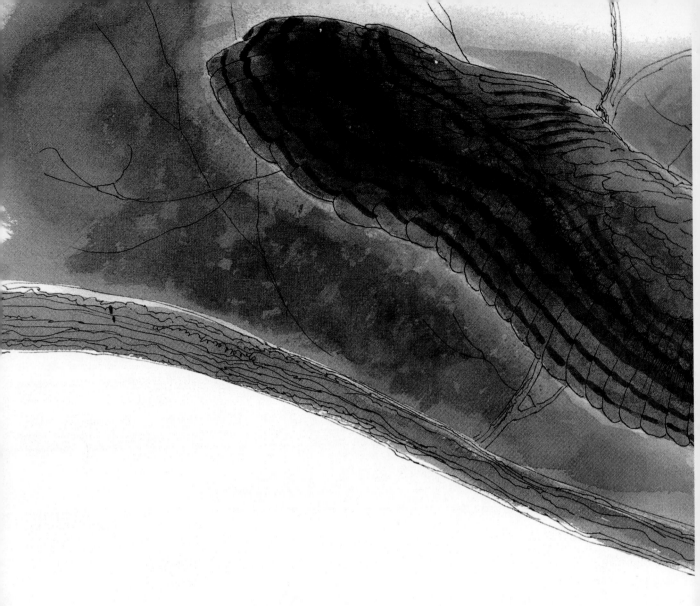

Pa turned on
his big flashlight
and caught the owl
just as it was landing
on a branch.

For one minute,
three minutes,
maybe even a hundred minutes,
we stared at one another.

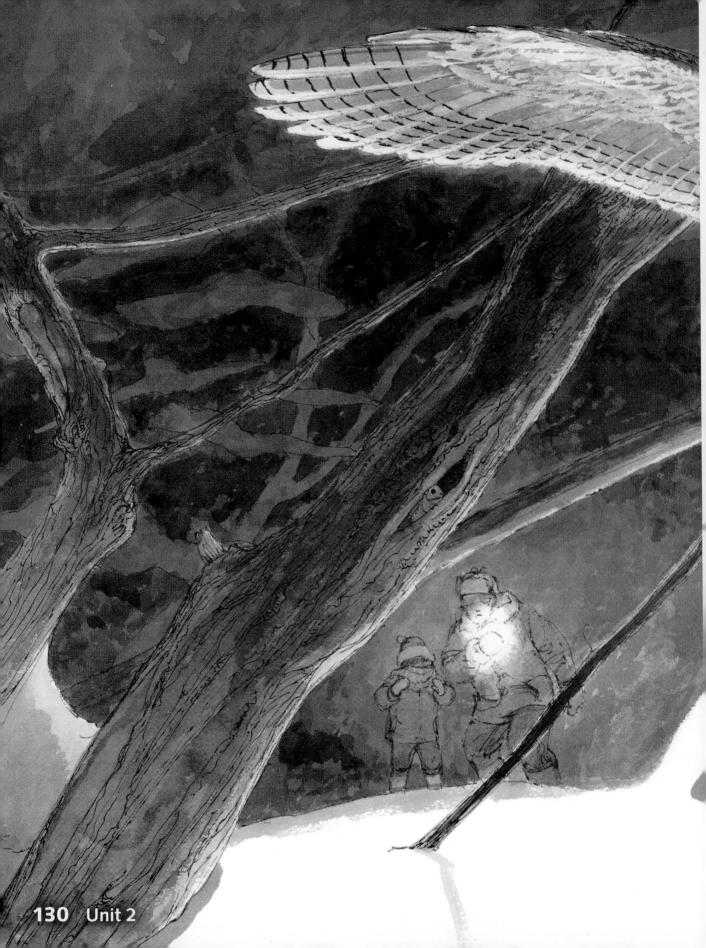

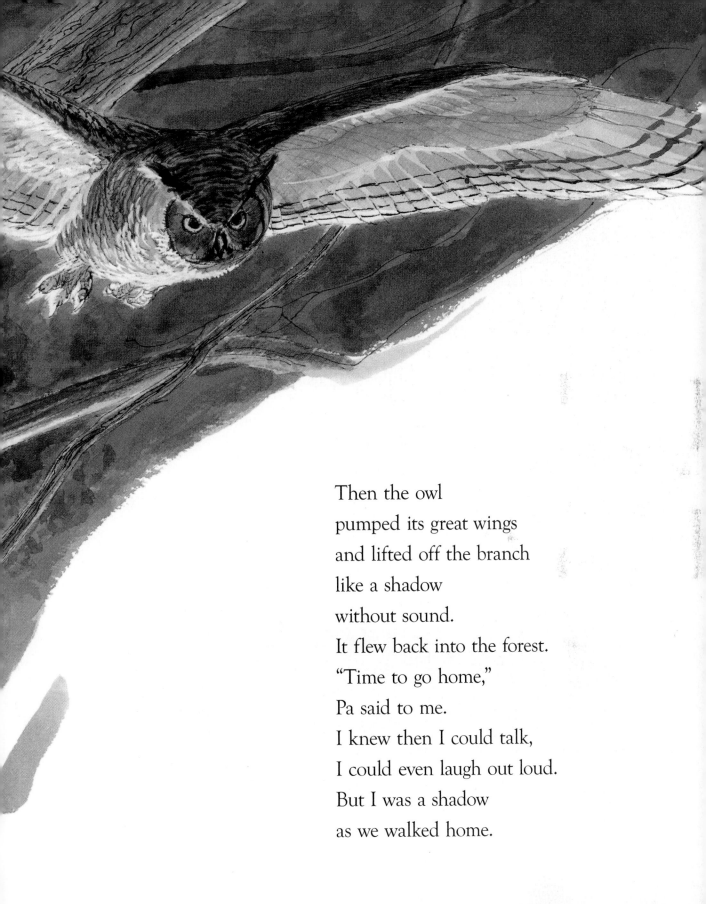

Then the owl
pumped its great wings
and lifted off the branch
like a shadow
without sound.
It flew back into the forest.
"Time to go home,"
Pa said to me.
I knew then I could talk,
I could even laugh out loud.
But I was a shadow
as we walked home.

When you go owling
you don't need words
or warm
or anything but hope.
That's what Pa says.
The kind of hope
that flies
on silent wings
under a shining
Owl Moon.

UNIT 3

The Shape of the Land

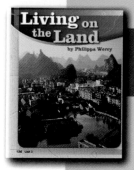

THEME Question

How does geography shape a community?

Focus Questions

How can we describe a community by its geography?

How do geography and natural resources affect a community?

How does geography affect how people work and play?

How is geography a foundation for a community?

Living on the Land

by Philippa Werry

Contents

Chapter 1

Looking Through the Window

Geography is the study of Earth and its people and features. Look out the window. What do you see? Do you see skyscrapers or mountains? Do you see the prairie or the ocean? What is the geography like where you live?

Many houses in San Francisco are built close together on the steep hills.

steps

Miami, Florida, is a community on the coast.

The land around a **community** is part of its geography. A community is a place where people live, work, and play. Communities can be found in the mountains, in the desert, on the coast, or on the plains. Each of these communities will be different.

Mountain Communities

Mountains are the highest of Earth's landforms. Mountain communities have to adapt to the steep, rugged land on a mountainside. They also have to cope with the cold climate.

Breckenridge, Colorado, is a mountain community. Many of the early buildings were made of wood from the mountain forests. It can get very cold in winter in Breckenridge. It often snows.

Most of the houses have steep roofs. Snow slides off steep roofs easily.

snow

This man is fly fishing on the Blue River in Breckenridge, Colorado.

Breckenridge formed when gold was discovered nearby. The gold mines closed, but Breckenridge continued to grow. The mountain area is good for skiing, hiking, fishing, or biking.

Desert Communities

A desert is a place where it doesn't rain much. Deserts can be very hot or very cold. The Painted Desert in northern Arizona is very hot and dry. A Hopi reservation and part of a Navajo reservation are in the desert in Arizona.

One of the biggest Navajo communities is in Tuba City, Arizona. Tuba City has freshwater springs. The Navajo use the water for growing crops.

The Navajo also use red clay from the area to make pottery.

hogan

A hogan is a traditional Navajo house. Most hogans are built from logs and covered with earth. A hogan has a door but no windows. It is cool in summer but warm in winter. Some hogans are still used today.

Coastal Communities

Many communities have formed in coastal places. The ocean can provide good food. These communities can also be useful for trade.

Cordova, Alaska, developed because oil and other minerals were discovered nearby. These things were mined and shipped from Cordova to other parts of the world. Today Cordova has a large fishing fleet and several fish factories.

The Trans Alaska Pipeline near Cordova transports oil across Alaska.

oil tanker

Cordova has lots of space to grow into, but some communities near the coast have little room to grow. More than one and a half million people live on Manhattan Island in New York City, New York. Subway trains travel underground. Buildings soar into the air.

Manhattan

Chinatown

Many people, such as the Chinese, have made their homes in small neighborhoods in and around New York City. These neighborhoods celebrate their culture and heritage.

This busy street is in the neighborhood of Chinatown, in New York City.

Plains Communities

Plains are wide, flat lands. Some of them are very grassy. Abilene, Kansas, is a city on the Great Plains. In the 1800s ranchers used the wide, open grasslands to run their cattle. Abilene had a railroad line. Ranchers drove their herds of cattle there so that they could be sent on trains to markets to be sold.

The railroad is still important for transporting goods to and from Abilene.

At first it was hard to live on the Great Plains. Many materials weren't available for building. Many people in these communities built their homes from sod.

Sod houses are made from squares of soil that have long grass roots in them. The grass roots make the squares strong.

The Great Plains are mostly flat and grassy, like this prairie in Wyoming.

fence post

Chapter 2

Geography and Work

Natural Resources

Geography and natural resources help shape **businesses** in a community. Natural resources are the useful things in nature, such as water, land, and even the wind.

Because it is on the coast and has lots of timber, Rockland, Maine, has a boat-building industry.

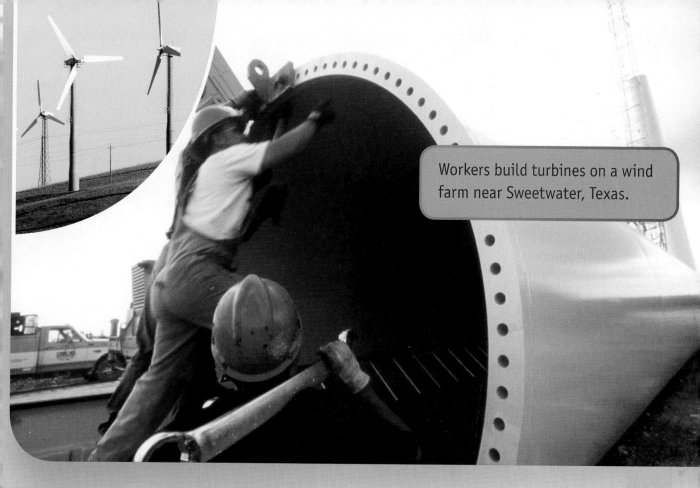

Workers build turbines on a wind farm near Sweetwater, Texas.

The Windy West

Wherever people live, they can use the natural resources around them. Sweetwater, Texas, is a town on the Great Plains. It's known for its strong winds. People decided to build wind turbines there. The turbines use the wind to make electricity. Many people in Sweetwater now have jobs building and taking care of turbines.

Flower Growers

North Carolina is a state that has rich, fertile soil. It's a great place for growing plants. In fact many people who live around Raleigh, North Carolina, grow flowers as their business.

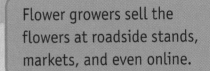

Flower growers sell the flowers at roadside stands, markets, and even online.

These logs in Longview, Washington, are tied together while they wait to be moved.

Timber!

The city of Longview, Washington, formed near a dense forest. It began as a single mill. People came to work there. Today Longview's lumber industry has grown much bigger. Longview also uses wood to produce paper—everything from grocery bags to envelopes.

What geography and natural resources does your community have? How do people use them?

Longview's lumber can be used for building houses.

Chapter 3

Geography in Everyday Life

Geography affects the things people do every day. People often choose their jobs based on where they live. Their surroundings even suggest ways of having fun. In this chapter you'll read about such communities.

This ranger works in a national park. She makes sure hikers and campers are safe.

The Power of Water

What would you do if farms needed water and there was a river close by? In the 1930s the government decided to build the Hoover Dam across the Colorado River between the states of Nevada and Arizona. Many people got jobs building the dam and keeping it in good order. That's how the town of Boulder City, Nevada, formed.

The Hoover Dam takes water from the river to use on farms and to produce electricity.

An Island Community

Nantucket, Massachusetts, was once very different from what it is today. This small island began as a whaling port. Whalers hunted sperm whales for their valuable oil. But by the mid-1800s there were few whales because they had been over-hunted. Many people began to use petroleum for fuel instead of whale oil. Nantucket's whaling industry soon came to an end.

From 1800 to 1830 Nantucket was one of the greatest whaling centers in the world.

sand

Many people take their vacation in Nantucket.

However, people found other ways to make a living on this beautiful island. Today **tourists** visit Nantucket to go fishing, boating, and swimming in the ocean. Many residents operate businesses that provide these activities for tourists.

Black Gold, Salt Fever

On January 10, 1901, oil shot out of the Lucas No. 1 well in Spindletop near Beaumont, Texas. People heard about the oil and raced to Beaumont to join the search. The town grew. Today Beaumont is the largest city in Jefferson County, Texas.

Once oil started shooting out of the Lucas No. 1 well, in Beaumont, Texas, it couldn't be stopped for nine days.

The Bonneville Salt Flats in the Great Salt Lake Desert, Utah, are the remains of an ancient lake.

People can think of amazing things to do because of an area's geography. Next to Wendover, Utah, is about 100 square miles of totally flat, empty land called the Bonneville Salt Flats. People use it for motor racing and breaking land speed records.

So how do people work and play in your community?

Chapter 4

Around the Globe

Geography affects where and how communities develop. It also affects how people in those communities live, work, and play.

Let's look at how three communities developed in different parts of the world.

Chinchero, Peru

Chinchero is a small **village** in the Andes Mountains in Peru, South America. It is so high up that it takes a while to get used to the thin air.

The Andes Mountains in Peru are very high and steep.

This is part of the church in Chinchero.

Most houses in Chinchero are made from mud bricks called adobe. The land is very steep, so the people have made terraces. That way, they have some flat land to grow crops.

The terraces in Chinchero are like these in nearby Sabandia, Peru.

Venice, Italy

Venice in Italy is one of the most unusual cities in the world. It is built in an area of saltwater called a lagoon. It has been cut off from the ocean by a reef, which is a ridge of rocks and sand.

Venice is built on more than 100 islands! Bridges join the islands. Instead of streets, there are canals. People travel by water taxi, ferryboat, or on foot.

canal

Many tourists ride around Venice in boats called gondolas.

From the 800s to the 1400s, ships from Venice set out to **trade** with cities in Europe and on other continents. Today, Venice is a popular place for tourists to visit.

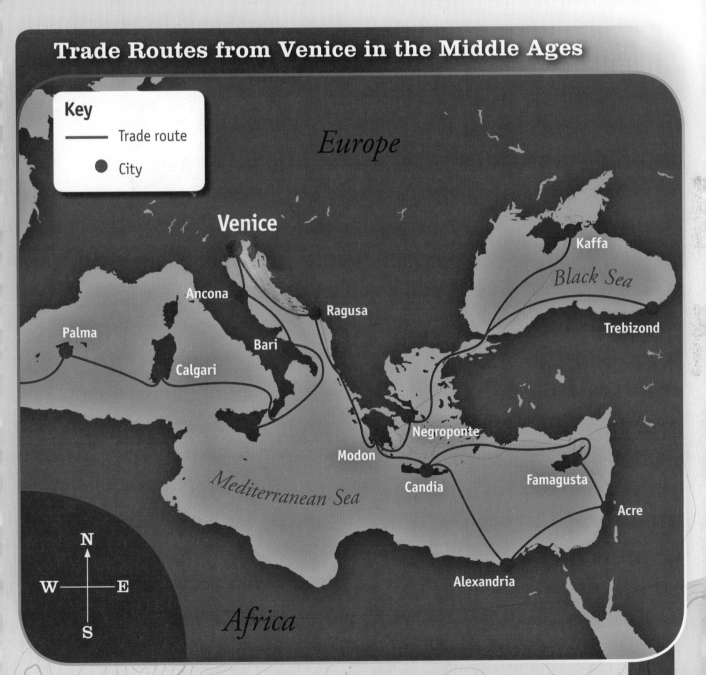

Trade Routes from Venice in the Middle Ages

Key

— Trade route

● City

Europe

Venice

Kaffa

Black Sea

Ancona

Ragusa

Trebizond

Palma

Bari

Calgari

Negroponte

Modon

Famagusta

Candia

Acre

Mediterranean Sea

Alexandria

N

W—E

S

Africa

Cairo, Egypt

Cairo is the biggest city in Egypt. It lies along the Nile River. In ancient times the river would often flood and leave silt, which is fine sand or mud, along the banks. Silt made the soil in the Nile River Valley very fertile. It was an important area for growing food.

The Nile River also made transportation easy. Today tourists visit ancient buildings around Cairo.

Nile River

pyramid

The Geography around You

You might not live in a big city, a port,
or a tourist center. But wherever you live,
the shape of the land affects your community.

Sum It Up

Communities form in many different places. A community might form on the coast, on the side of a mountain, beside a lake, or in a desert. The geography of a place affects the communities that form there. It affects how people live, work, and have fun.

How does the geography of your community affect your life?

Tops & Bottoms

Adapted and illustrated by
JANET STEVENS

Once upon a time there lived a very lazy bear who had lots of money and lots of land. His father had been a hard worker and a smart business bear, and he had given all of his **wealth** to his son.

But all Bear wanted to do was sleep.

Not far down the road lived a hare. Although Hare was clever, he sometimes got into trouble. He had once owned land, too, but now he had nothing. He had lost a risky bet with a tortoise and had sold all of his land to Bear to pay off the debt.

Hare and his family were in very bad shape. "The children are so hungry, Father Hare! We must think of something!" Mrs. Hare cried one day. So Hare and Mrs. Hare put their heads together and cooked up a plan.

The next day Hare hopped down the road to Bear's house. Bear, of course, was asleep.

"Hello, Bear, wake up! It's your neighbor, Hare, and I have an idea!"

Bear opened one eye and grunted.

"We can be business partners!" Hare said. "All we need is this field right here in front of your house. I'll do the hard work of planting and harvesting, and we can split the profit right down the middle. Yes, sir, Bear, we're in this together. I'll work and you sleep."

"Huh?" said Bear.

"So, what will it be, Bear?" asked Hare. "The top half or the bottom half? It's up to you—tops or bottoms."

"Uh, let's see," Bear said with a yawn. "I'll take the top half, Hare. Right—tops."

Hare smiled. "It's a done deal, Bear."

Tops & Bottoms   **169**

So Bear went back to sleep, and Hare and his family went to work. Hare planted, Mrs. Hare watered, and everyone weeded.

Bear slept as the crops grew.

When it was time for the harvest, Hare called out,
"Wake up, Bear! You get the tops and I get the bottoms."

Hare and his family dug up the carrots, the radishes, and the beets. Hare plucked off all the tops, tossed them into a pile for Bear, and put the bottoms aside for himself.

Bear stared at his pile. "But, Hare, all the best parts are in your half!"

"You chose the tops, Bear," Hare said.
"Now, Hare, you've tricked me. You
plant this field again—and this season
I want the bottoms!"

Hare agreed. "It's a done deal, Bear."

So Bear went back to sleep, and Hare and his family went to work. They planted, watered, and weeded.

Bear slept as the crops grew.

When it was time for the harvest, Hare called out, "Wake up, Bear! You get the bottoms and I get the tops."

Hare and his family gathered up the lettuce, the broccoli, and the celery. Hare pulled off the bottoms for Bear and put the tops in his own pile.

Bear looked at his pile and scowled.
"Hare, you have cheated me again."

"But, Bear," Hare said, "you wanted the bottoms this time."

Bear growled, "You plant this field again, Hare. You've tricked me twice, and you **owe** me one season of both tops and bottoms!"

"You're right, poor old Bear," sighed Hare. "It's only fair that you get both tops and bottoms this time. It's a done deal, Bear."

So Bear went back to sleep, and Hare and his family went to work. They planted, watered, and weeded, then watered and weeded some more.

Bear slept as the crops grew.

When it was time for the harvest, Hare called out, "Wake up, Bear! This time you get the tops and the bottoms!"

There in front of Bear's house lay a high field of corn. Hare and his family yanked up every cornstalk. Hare tugged off the roots at the bottom and the tassels at the top and put them in a pile for Bear. Then he carefully collected the ears of corn in the middle and placed them in his own pile.

Bear rubbed his eyes and watched.

"See, Bear? You get the tops and the bottoms. I get the middles. Yes, sir, Bear. It's a done deal!"

By now Bear was wide awake. "That's it, Hare!" he hollered. "From now on I'll plant my own crops and take the tops, bottoms, and middles!"

Hare and his family scooped up the corn and hopped down the road toward home.

Bear never again slept through a season of planting and harvesting. Hare bought back his land with the profit from the crops, and he and Mrs. Hare opened a vegetable stand.

And although Hare and Bear learned to live happily as neighbors, they never became business partners again!

Digging Up a Story

What is the story of the Earth?

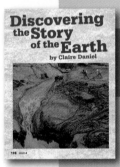

Discovering the Story of the Earth
Nonfiction: Informational Text

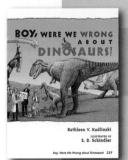

Boy, Were We Wrong About Dinosaurs!
Nonfiction: Informational Text

THEME Question

What is the story of the Earth?

Focus Questions

What do we learn when we look below Earth's surface?

What role does water play in the story of Earth?

How are humans part of
Earth's story?

How does Earth's surface
give us clues to the past?

Discovering the Story of the Earth

by Claire Daniel

Contents

Chapter 1
Digging Deep

Imagine digging a deep hole in your yard. What do you think you would find—maybe buried treasure? You'd probably find only dirt and stones.

If you could dig down far into Earth, you'd see many **layers**. These layers would tell you a lot about the fascinating story of our planet.

spade

This photograph shows part of the ocean floor.

Earth has many layers, so we say it is multilayered. The first layer of Earth is called the crust. It is made up of rock. In some places the crust is between three and six miles thick. In other places it can be more than 40 miles thick! It is amazing how deep it goes! The ocean floor is also part of Earth's crust.

# To the Center of the Earth

Beneath Earth's crust is the mantle. There are two layers in the mantle. The top layer is solid. The bottom layer is hot, and it is partially melted. Something that is melted by heat is called molten.

Earth's Layers

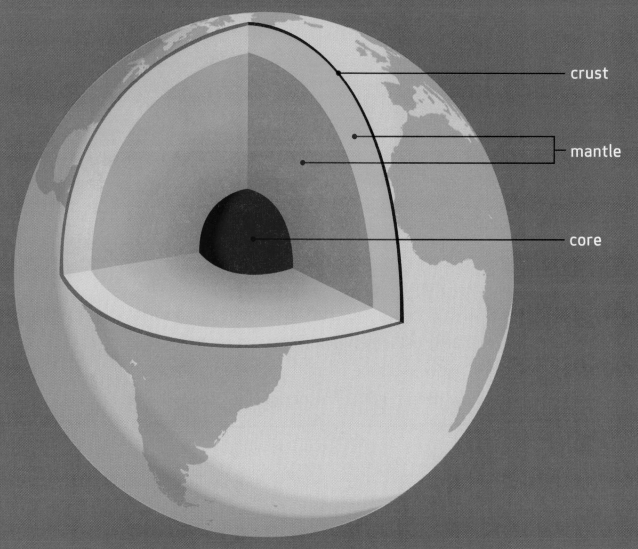

crust

mantle

core

You would have to travel down 1,800 miles to get through Earth's mantle. Then you would reach Earth's core. The outside of the core is molten too. But the inside is solid and really hot—about as hot as the surface of the sun!

A worker uses a drill to explore Earth's crust.

We're Moving

You might be surprised to learn that Earth's crust and the upper layer of the mantle are moving. These two layers are made up of huge slabs of rock called plates. The plates cover Earth. They move very slowly over the lower mantle.

Over millions of years the plates have drifted apart. They have slid past one another or pushed against each other. This movement slowly created mountains and valleys. It caused volcanoes to erupt. It even caused earthquakes to open up the ground. And the plates are still moving!

Plate A is moving over Plate B.
Plate B is sliding under Plate A.

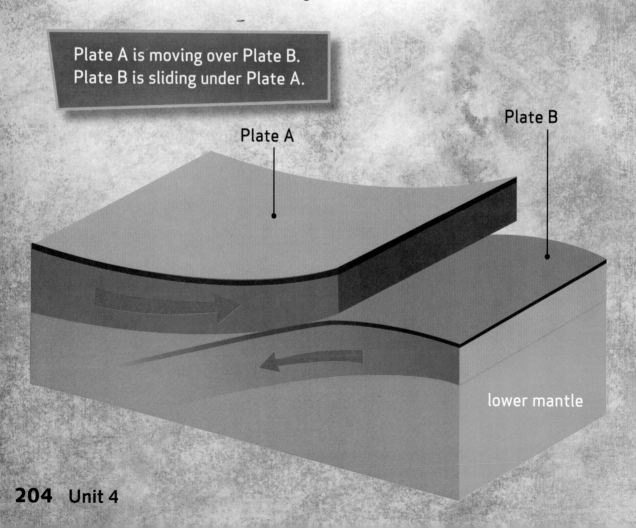

Plate A

Plate B

lower mantle

Most earthquakes happen along faults, which are cracks in Earth's crust. This photo shows the San Andreas Fault in California.

fossilized dinosaur bones

Scientists can figure out how Earth's landscape has changed by studying **fossils**. Fossils are the remains of plants and animals that lived in the distant past. Fossils are found in rocks in Earth's crust. Scientists have found fossils of the same kind of plant in many different parts of the world.

This scientist is carefully brushing away dirt from a fossil.

This oil rig is drilling for oil under the ocean floor.

 **Fossil Fuels**

Like fossils, fossil fuels are formed from the remains of dead plants and animals. These plants and animals lived many years ago. Coal, natural gas, and crude oil are all fossil fuels. They are found deep inside Earth. They are mined from the ground or beneath the ocean.

Chapter 2
Running Water, Moving Ice

Water plays an important role in shaping and changing Earth. It is always on the move—in rivers, lakes, and oceans, and in the sky. Water that falls from the sky is called precipitation. Rain, snow, mist, and hail are all kinds of precipitation.

Water on Earth is never used up. As you have learned, it moves around and around in a cycle.

Every living thing needs water, from plants to people.

Let's take a closer look at the water cycle. When the sun heats water on Earth's surface, the water changes into a gas called water vapor. The vapor rises into the sky. As it rises, it gets cooler and turns into tiny droplets. These droplets form clouds, which get denser and colder. The droplets join together to form bigger drops of water. They fall to Earth again as precipitation.

The Water Cycle

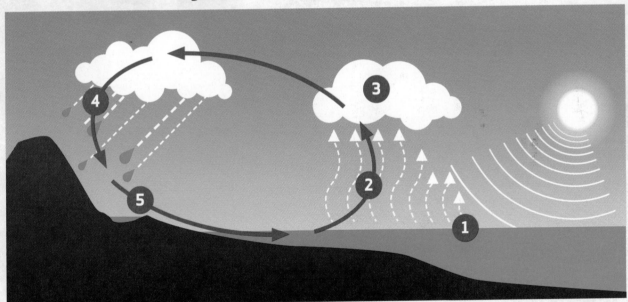

1 Water turns into vapor.

2 Water vapor rises.

3 Clouds form.

4 Precipitation falls on the land.

5 Water flows into rivers, lakes, and oceans.

Rivers and Rainwater

Over millions of years, moving water changes Earth's surface. Rivers can cut into rock to make valleys or deep canyons.

Water also washes soil and rock from hills and mountains down onto plains. Large rivers often carry soil to where the river meets the ocean or a lake. This soil can form a triangle of land called a delta.

A river has formed a deep canyon in this rock.

This image of the Mississippi River Delta was taken by a satellite.

Mississippi River

Mississippi River Delta

Rainwater **trickles** through cracks in the ground and down into Earth. Over time the water wears away the rock and soil. It makes tunnels or caves. Most large caves form in a soft rock called limestone.

Underground Caves

In some caves stalactites hang from the roof or walls. Stalactites are formed when water drips through the ceiling of a cave. The water leaves behind a small amount of a mineral. Slowly the stalactite grows down, like an icicle. Stalagmites grow up when water drips onto the cave floor.

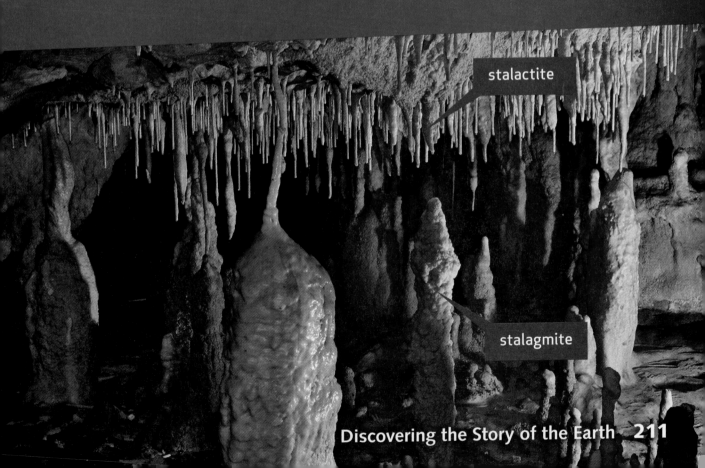

stalactite

stalagmite

Glaciers and Fjords

Some water moves very slowly. Glaciers are rivers of ice. They creep downhill over hundreds of years. As they move, they carve deep valleys in the rock. Glaciers can even push huge rocks along.

Some glaciers have lasted for thousands of years. They have carved out deep valleys in the mountains.

This fjord is near Olden, Norway.

Over many centuries a glacier can carve a long, narrow valley all the way down to the ocean. Sometimes the glacier melts. Then the valley can fill with seawater. This sea-filled valley is called a fjord (fee*ORD*). Many fjords have very steep sides. They can be thousands of feet deep.

Chapter 3
Earth's Storytellers

Some people study Earth to find out about its history.

Geologists are scientists who study what Earth is made from and how it changes. Some geologists study the layers of rocks to find out what was happening on Earth a long time ago.

The Grand Canyon, in the southwestern United States, is about a mile deep. In its walls you can see more than 40 layers of rock.

Archaeologists have to be very careful when they dig up things from long ago.

It can be hard to discover how **ancient** people lived. The places where they lived have been buried for thousands of years. Archaeologists study how ancient people lived. They look at ancient tools, clothing, and art. Each of these things is like a piece in a jigsaw puzzle. Every piece is a part of the whole picture. Archaeologists put the pieces together to understand what life was once like.

Fossil Hunters

Some scientists look even further back in time. They study the fossils of animals and plants buried in rock. These scientists are called paleontologists.

This shell fossil tells scientists that this land was once part of the ocean.

bone

This paleontologist finds 30,000-year-old fossils near the leg bone of a large animal from before the last ice age.

Fossils can show paleontologists what food an ancient animal, such as a dinosaur, might've eaten. For example, some dinosaur fossils have teeth that were good for chewing plants. The fossils of the meat-eating dinosaurs, such as *Tyrannosaurus rex*, tend to have large back leg bones and sharp claws. Their legs helped them run fast. Their claws helped them catch prey.

Earth's Changing Story

Today many things that people do are changing Earth's story. We mine Earth for minerals such as silver, gold, and copper. We dig into Earth to get fossil fuels. We burn coal for electricity. All of these things change Earth. They have an effect on the **environment**.

coal

In Utah, copper is mined at a large open-pit mine called Bingham Canyon Mine.

Imagine that it is millions of years in the future. An archaeologist could be digging where you once lived. What interesting things might an archaeologist find in your home? What might these things tell people about how you live today?

Winds of Change

Fossil fuels are also used to make the gasoline that we use to run cars.

As fossil fuels such as oil and coal become scarce, people need to use other sources of energy. Giant windmills called turbines can use the wind to make electricity.

Chapter 4
Earth at Your Feet

You don't have to dig deep to find out about Earth. Some of Earth's story is right under your feet. You can find out a lot just by looking closely at the rocks and the soil.

The pebbles on a beach may be washed up by the ocean or worn away from ocean cliffs.

Most grains of sand were once parts of solid rocks.

sand

Over time rocks are worn down by wind, rain, running water, and glaciers. Water from rivers and streams carries away small bits that have broken off. These tiny pieces of rock can end up as the sand on a beach. They can also mix with other things to make soil.

Look Closer

You can use a magnifying glass to look at soil. You might see tiny pieces of rock, plants, or insects. Each kind of soil has different amounts of these things. This provides good food for the plants growing there.

magnifying glass

The soil in this forest is covered with rotting leaves.

The red soil in this Australian desert is rich in iron.

Maybe the soil outside your home is red. The color of the soil depends on the kind of rock and amount of decayed material it has come from. Red soil was made from rock that had a lot of iron in it. Iron is a hard mineral from which steel is made.

# A Rock's Journey

Rocks move in a slow journey that may never really end! The plates of rock that move on Earth's crust and upper mantle drag pieces of rock beneath the surface. The rock changes. It is melted by the heat from the center of Earth.

Many of the rocks in and around Mount St. Helens, in Washington State, were formed inside Earth long ago.

Some of the changed rock is pushed up to Earth's surface where it forms hills and mountains. Then some is forced out as melted rock when a volcano erupts. This rock is broken up by wind and water. Then the rock is dragged beneath the surface again. This journey is called the rock cycle.

This photograph shows a volcano erupting.

The Rock Cycle

3 volcano erupts

4 wind and water break up rock

1 rock dragged beneath the ground

2 rock melts

Sum It Up

The story of Earth changes all the time. Moving plates and water change Earth's surface. Wind, heat, and cold change things too. So do people, plants, and animals.

Next time you go outside, look around carefully. Think about all the fossils that could be buried under your feet. Think about how rain droplets form. Everything around you is a part of Earth's story.

BOY, WERE WE WRONG ABOUT DINOSAURS!

Kathleen V. Kudlinski

ILLUSTRATED BY
S. D. Schindler

LONG, LONG AGO, before people knew anything about dinosaurs, giant bones were found in China. Wise men who saw the bones tried to guess what sort of **enormous** animal they could have come from.

After they studied the fossil bones, the ancient
Chinese decided that they came from dragons. They
thought these dragons must have been magic dragons
to be so large. And they believed that dragons could
still be alive.

Boy, were they wrong!

No one knows exactly what dinosaurs looked like. All that is left of them are fossil bones and a few other **clues**. Now we think that many of our own past guesses about dinosaurs were just as wrong as those of ancient China.

Some of our mistakes were little ones. When the first fossil bones of *Iguanodon* were found, one was shaped like a rhino's horn. Scientists guessed that the strange bone fit like a spike on *Iguanodon*'s nose.

Boy, were we wrong about *Iguanodon*!

When a full set of fossil bones was found later, there were *two* pointed bones. They were part of *Iguanodon*'s hands, not its nose!

Other new clues show us that we may have been wrong about every kind of dinosaur.

Some of our first drawings of dinosaurs showed them with their elbows and knees pointing out to the side, like a lizard's. With legs like that, big dinosaurs could only waddle clumsily on all fours or float underwater.

Now we know their legs were straight under them, like a horse's. Dinosaurs were not clumsy. The sizes and shapes of their leg bones seem to show that some were as fast and graceful as deer.

Paintings in old books show dinosaurs dragging their tails in the dirt because a few fossils of tail drags were found. And scientists couldn't imagine how muscles could hold up the enormous tails.

Thousands of fossil footprints have now been found with no tail drag marks at all. Clues in some dinosaur fossils show that their tailbones had stiff tendons inside to help hold them out straight. With their heavy tails to provide balance, many dinosaurs, even giant *Apatosaurus,* could probably stand on their hind legs, reaching leaves in the tallest trees. Others, like *Tyrannosaurus,* always walked on two legs.

DINOSAUR

LIZARD

Inside the bones, scientists have found surprises, too. We used to think that dinosaurs were cold-blooded, like snakes and lizards. Cold-blooded animals need to bask in the sun to warm their bodies. When scientists look through a microscope at slices of lizard bones, they don't see many blood vessels inside. They do see rings where new bone grew slowly year by year.

Dinosaur bones look different. They have lots of blood vessels inside, and new bone seems to grow around every one of them.

Dinosaurs may have been more like birds, with bodies that were warm and full of energy, night and day. They would have needed this extra energy to move their graceful legs.

Are we right about dinosaurs yet? Now some scientists think they were neither cold-blooded nor warm-blooded, but something in between. There is no way to be sure.

Scientists used to think all dinosaurs were scaly, because a few fossil skins showed bumps that look like scales. Now more fossils have been found with marks that seem to be from feathers. What did dinosaurs have on their skin: bumps, scales, or feathers? We can only guess, but we have some good ideas.

Because big animals lose heat more slowly, we think that the big dinosaurs, like the big elephants of today, wouldn't have needed fur or feathers to keep themselves warm.

In the last few years, fossils of many kinds of little dinosaurs have been found. Some grew no bigger than pigeons. These small animals needed some way to keep from losing their body heat. Some of the fossils show warm, fluffy feathers like a baby chick's. Others show long feathers like a rooster's.

Scientists used to think that large dinosaurs were gray, like today's gray elephants. But if that were true, bigger meat-eating dinosaurs would be able to see these gray dinosaurs against colorful leaves and grasses, and they would be eaten. Now scientists think that dinosaurs had colorful patterns that protected them from being found and eaten. Colors and patterns also probably helped dinosaurs show their sex and age to other dinosaurs, the way birds do.

Recent X-rays of some dinosaur fossils show that they had birdlike skulls, with room for large eyes and enough brain space for color vision.

We used to think that dinosaur mothers
acted like lizard mothers. Boy, were we wrong!
Lizards just lay their eggs on the ground, then
leave. They never see their own babies.

Now we have found fossil dinosaur eggs in fossil nests. Some of the nests hold newly hatched babies. Other nests are packed tightly with older baby dinosaurs. These youngsters have scratches on their teeth from eating tough plants. Did their mothers bring food back to the nest? Or did the young go out to feed, then come back home to sleep? We can only guess, but these are things that lizards never do.

In one place, many nests of fossil dinosaur eggs have been found on a hill. It must have been a safe place, because different kinds of dinosaur mothers made their nests there year after year.

Fossil footprints have been found that show a whole herd of dinosaurs walking together. Footprints of baby dinosaurs are there, too, walking safely in the middle of the herd. So we know some dinosaurs took good care of their babies.

Even our ideas about the end of the dinosaurs seem to have been wrong. Scientists used to think that the world slowly dried out or got hotter and that heat and disease killed every dinosaur.

In the last few years, we have found a fossil layer of dust that is probably from outer space. This new clue makes us think a comet or asteroid might have hit the Earth and exploded, setting off fires and tidal waves. It could have made a huge dust cloud that would have poisoned the rain and blocked the sunshine for years.

Most plants can't grow without sunlight. And acid rain
makes plants and animals weak and sick. If the plants all
died, the animals that ate those plants couldn't find food.
And if those animals died, the meat-eaters wouldn't have
any food, either.

Scientists think all this might have happened before the
cloud settled to a thick layer of dust on the earth. But we
could still be wrong about the end of the dinosaurs.

Boy, Were We Wrong about Dinosaurs! 251

In one way, the scientists of today agree with the Chinese of long ago. They believe some dinosaurs are still alive. Toward the end of the millions and millions of years that dinosaurs lived on Earth, some of the smaller, feathered kinds changed bit by bit.

Over the years, their feathers became longer. They began to fly. Gradually, they became birds. While the rest of the dinosaurs died out, somehow some of these birds survived. If scientists are right, our birds are living dinosaurs.

There are still dinosaur books in libraries and
bookstores that show the old ways of thinking.
Scientists keep finding new clues, and our thinking
has to change. Perhaps today's ideas about dinosaurs
will someday seem just as silly as the magic dragons of
long-ago China.

When you grow up, you may be the scientist
who makes us all say, "Boy, were we wrong
about dinosaurs!"

A DINOSAUR DISCOVERY TIMELINE

1822	Gideon Mantell, a British doctor, names an ancient animal *Iguanodon*.
1842	Richard Owen, an English anatomist and paleontologist, comes up with the term *Dinosauria*, or "great reptile."
1923	Explorer Roy Chapman Andrews finds dinosaur eggs in the Gobi Desert.
1964	Paleontologist John H. Ostrom questions the cold-bloodedness of dinosaurs.
1968	Paleontologist Robert Bakker draws dinosaurs standing straight with tails upheld.
1973	John H. Ostrom says birds are dinosaurs.
1970's	Walter Alvarez, a geologist, discovers a thin layer of iridium dust.
1978	Jack Horner finds dinosaur nests with fossil young still in them.
1999	Xiao-Chun Wu and Mark Norell both find feathered dinosaur fossils in China.

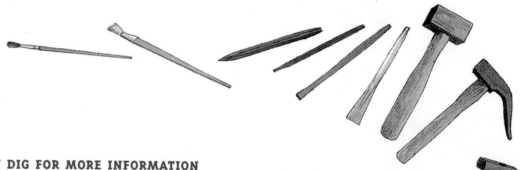

WHERE YOU CAN DIG FOR MORE INFORMATION

Norman, David, et al. *Eyewitness: Dinosaurs.* New York: DK Publishing, 2000.
    Basic dinosaur facts and photos of fossils.

Lambert, David, et al. *Dinosaur Encyclopedia: From Dinosaurs to the Dawn of Man.*
    New York: DK Publishing, 2001. Answers every possible question on the subject.

A FEW OF THE WORKS USED IN THE RESEARCH FOR THIS BOOK

Farlow, James, and M. K. Brett-Surman, eds. *The Complete Dinosaur.*
    Bloomington, IN: Indiana University Press, 1997.

Horner, John. *Digging Dinosaurs.* New York: Workman Publishing Company, 1988.

Lucas, Spencer G. *Dinosaurs: The Textbook.* New York: McGraw-Hill
    Professional Publishing, 1996.

THANKS TO THE SCIENTISTS WHO HELPED IN THE WRITING OF THIS BOOK

Daniel Lee Brinkman, Peabody Museum of Natural History, Yale University.

Byron Butler, Peabody Museum of Natural History, Yale University.

Mark Norell, chairman and curator, Division of Paleontology, American Museum
    of Natural History, New York City.

Heroes Across Time

THEME
Question

What qualities does a hero have?

Focus Questions

Why do we tell stories about heroes from the past?

Why do we make up stories about heroes?

Can an ordinary person be a hero?

What makes a hero?

Heroes

By Georgina Scott

Superhero

Mountain climber

Firefighter

Tree planters

Contents

Sports star

CHAPTER 1

Heroes of a Nation

Who are the heroes from the past? Soldiers who fought in wars are often called heroes. Explorers who sailed across oceans in search of adventure and new lands are also often called heroes. Great athletes are sometimes called heroes too.

Amazing U.S. athlete "Babe" Didrikson Zaharias won three Olympic medals in 1932. ▶

▼ From 1804 to 1806, Lewis and Clark led a team of explorers.

▲ Dr. Martin Luther King, Jr. spoke about equal rights for African Americans.

People have different ideas about what a hero is. However, most agree that heroes have courage. Courage means acting boldly even when you're afraid. It means standing up for what you believe is right even when others say you are wrong. Courageous people change the course of history.

Ellen Ochoa has completed four missions in space as a U.S. astronaut. ▶

The Giant

Abraham Lincoln (1809–1865)

Abraham Lincoln was 6 feet, 4 inches tall. To some people, he looked like a giant! He was a giant in United States history too.

When Lincoln won the election for president in 1860, many Southern states broke away from the United States. The Civil War began the next year, and hundreds of thousands of soldiers were killed in battle.

▼ In the first battle of the Civil War, at Manassas in Virginia, around 5,000 men were killed or wounded.

▲ Enslaved African Americans were often sold at auctions.

Many people disagreed with Lincoln's idea that slavery was wrong. They wanted enslaved people to work on farms and in their houses. But Lincoln stayed calm and showed great patience.

The war ended in 1865. The states in the South were in ruins, but over the next few months, all of the enslaved people were freed. Lincoln's leadership and determination had helped put an end to slavery.

The Risk Taker

Susie King Taylor (1848–1912)

Susie King Taylor was just twelve when the Civil War began in 1861. In 1862 Taylor and enslaved people like her ran away. They left their homes in Savannah, Georgia, in order to gain their freedom. Taylor went with her uncle and his family to St. Simon's Island.

Taylor knew how to read and write, so she was asked to organize a school on the island. During the day she taught forty children. At night she taught adults to read.

▼ Many enslaved people traveled by land to St. Catherine's Island and then by boat to St. Simon's Island.

The Route to Saint Simon's Island

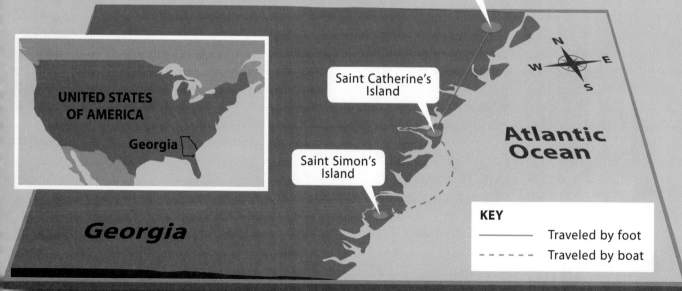

UNITED STATES OF AMERICA

Georgia

Georgia

Savannah

Saint Catherine's Island

Saint Simon's Island

Atlantic Ocean

KEY
——— Traveled by foot
- - - - - Traveled by boat

After she left the island, Taylor helped soldiers of the First South Carolina Volunteers fighting in the war. It was a daring move because she was still very young. Taylor worked as a nurse. She also taught soldiers to read and write.

Many African Americans were soldiers of the First South Carolina Volunteers. ▲

When the war ended, Taylor went back to Savannah and started a school for black children who had been freed from slavery.

Taylor took great risks by helping people. Her courage made many lives better.

Taylor was the only African American woman to write a book about her experiences in the Civil War. ▶

REMINISCENCES OF
MY LIFE IN CAMP

WITH THE 33D UNITED STATES
COLORED TROOPS LATE 1ST
S. C. VOLUNTEERS

BY

SUSIE KING TAYLOR

WITH ILLUSTRATIONS

BOSTON
PUBLISHED BY THE AUTHOR
1902

Fight No More

Chief Joseph (approx. 1840–1904)

Chief Joseph was the leader of a group of Native Americans called the Nez Perce. In the 1870s the United States government told Chief Joseph to move his people away from their homeland so white settlers could have the land. Chief Joseph said they would not leave. In 1877 a war broke out after warriors killed some of the settlers.

Chief Joseph knew he had to find safety for his people, so he led them away from United States troops.

▼ This map shows the route taken by Chief Joseph and the Nez Perce people.

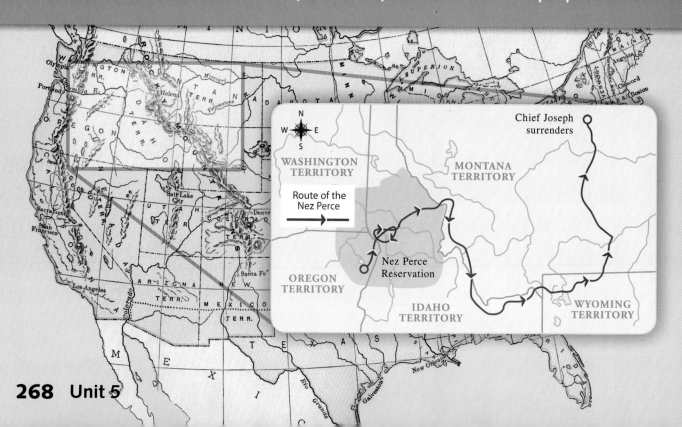

▲ Chief Joseph and the Nez Perce warriors surrender in 1877 at Bear Paw Battlefield in Montana Territory.

The army followed them for more than 1,000 miles. The Nez Perce warriors were **tough** and fought bravely, but more and more of them were killed.

Finally, Chief Joseph surrendered. He knew that fighting would not lead to victory. He said, "I am tired. My heart is sick and sad. From where the sun now stands, I will fight no more forever."

This photo shows ▶ Chief Joseph in 1900.

The Baseball Player

Roberto Clemente   (1934–1972)

Roberto Clemente was a skillful athlete and an extraordinary baseball player. His career with Major League Baseball began in 1955. After his last game in 1972, he had four awards for batting and twelve for fielding.

But it was Clemente's kindness that made him a hero. He helped children and other baseball players improve their games.

▼ Clemente talks with young baseball players at a stadium in Pennsylvania.

▲ Clemente scores a home run for his team, the Pittsburgh Pirates.

When the 1972 season was over, Clemente returned to Puerto Rico to help at a children's sports camp. Then an earthquake caused **terrible** damage in the nearby country of Nicaragua. Clemente gathered supplies and boarded a plane to help the people who were hurt in the earthquake. Tragically, the plane crashed as it was taking off. Clemente did not survive.

Every year a Major League player receives the Roberto Clemente Award. In 2006 Carlos Delgado received the award for his work in the community. ▶

CHAPTER 2

Heroes in Stories

The heroes in made-up stories are out of the ordinary. They often have amazing strength or special powers. They do things that seem impossible to us.

People tell different kinds of stories about heroes. Myths are told to explain why or how things happened. In myths heroes often face an impossible **challenge**.

Diana, goddess of the hunt, is a character from Roman mythology. ▲

Folktales are stories that have been told again and again. They may be true, but they have changed a lot. The characters are lively and memorable.

The folk hero Johnny Appleseed was a real person named John Chapman. ▶

Legends are stories of heroes from long ago. No one is sure if they are true.

All of these stories—true or not—inspire us and help us to understand what it means to be a hero.

In an English legend, Arthur pulled a sword out of a stone and became king. ▲

John Henry is a folk hero who could work faster than a machine. ▶

Legend

Hua Mulan

The story of Hua Mulan is a legend. In this legend Hua Mulan's father was told to go fight in a war between two peoples in China, but he was too old and weak to fight. Someone needed to go in his place. Mulan was loyal to both her father and her country. So she gathered all her courage, dressed as a man, and went to fight in the war.

For twelve years none of the soldiers found out that Mulan was really a girl. When the war was over, the emperor wanted to reward her.

Many statues of Hua ▶
Mulan have been put up in China.

Folktale

"Casey" Jones (1864–1900)

Casey Jones's real name was John Luther Jones. He got his nickname from the name of the town he grew up in—Cayce, Kentucky. As a young man, Jones got a job as a railroad engineer.

One night, Jones realized his train was going to crash into a freight train. Jones stayed in the cab and tried to stop his train, but there was still a terrible crash. Casey Jones saved everyone on the train, but the accident caused his death.

▲ Casey Jones became famous for his quick thinking and bravery.

Jones is in the cab of his engine. ▼

Myth

Prometheus

Prometheus was stronger than a storm and smarter than a snake . . . but some said he was a troublemaker.

The god Zeus didn't want human beings to have any power.

NEVER give humans fire.

But they need it.

They can't cook. They are cold.

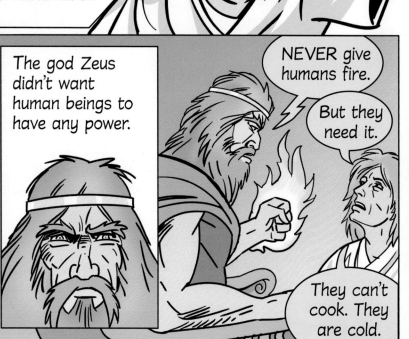

Prometheus could see that the people were suffering.

I HAVE to help.

One night, Prometheus climbed up and lit a torch from the Sun's fire.

He carried the torch back down the mountain and passed it to the people.

You've SAVED us!

When Zeus found out, he wasn't happy.

How dare you disobey me!

Zeus chained poor Prometheus to a rock.

Suffer for all time!

NOOO!

An eagle swooped down and attacked Prometheus.

Every day the eagle came back. Prometheus was immortal, which meant that he could not die. So he felt the same awful pain for hundreds of years.

Finally, Prometheus was rescued by his second cousin, Hercules.

Hercules shot the eagle.

Prometheus was finally free!

I thought I'd be there forever!

He was weary and had suffered greatly.

However, his act of bravery and kindness had given the people heat and light.

CHAPTER 3

Everyday Heroes

Have you ever met a hero? You may have without knowing it. Many people do heroic things every day. They might not wear superhero costumes, but they make a difference in people's lives and in the world. They have determination. The size of the job doesn't matter because a hero will get things done!

A young girl takes care of her grandfather. ▲

▼ Many people think of doctors as heroes.

doctor

patient

flames

hose

▲ Every day firefighters risk their lives to help people.

Some people are seen as heroes for doing one **amazing** thing. They become a champion for a day. Other people work quietly, sometimes for years and sometimes all their lives. They are trying hard to change the world— one day at a time.

Beginning when she was 35 years old, Mother Teresa worked to help the poor in India. ▶

Well Maker

Ryan Hreljac (1991–   )

In 1998, when he was in first grade, Ryan found that some children in poor countries didn't have clean water to drink. He began working hard to raise money so that he could help to build a well.

▲ This is a photo of Ryan at nine years old.

"I have learned that you can do anything you want to, but only if you really try hard and really want to."

Ryan's first well was built a year later in a small village in Uganda, Africa. Today thousands of people use this well.

Now Ryan has his own organization called Ryan's Well Foundation. It has built more than 400 wells in 16 countries.

◄ This photo is of Ryan in Uganda when he was 15 years old.

Magazine Publisher

Christianne Meneses Jacobs (1971–)

Christianne Meneses Jacobs was born in Nicaragua. When she was a teenager, she moved to California. Even though she lived in a new country, Christianne was proud of her heritage.

When she was older, Jacobs decided to start a children's magazine written in Spanish. During the day Jacobs worked as a teacher.

"You have to believe in yourself—and work really hard too."

She learned all she could about magazine publishing. Then she launched *Iguana* magazine. It has been a great success.

Jacobs has now launched a second magazine called *¡YO SÉ!*

▲ *Iguana* is a magazine written in Spanish for children ages seven to twelve.

Peacemaker

Sadako Sasaki (1943–1955)

In 1945 an atomic bomb was dropped on the city of Hiroshima, Japan. The bomb made a young girl named Sadako Sasaki sick with cancer. A friend told her an old Japanese belief that a person who makes one thousand paper cranes is granted a wish. Sadako wished to get well, and she began to fold paper cranes.

"I will write peace on your wings, and you will fly all over the world."

While fighting her illness, she folded hundreds of paper cranes. However, she continued to get weaker and died in October 1955. People all over the world today still feel inspired by her message.

◄ Every year on August 6th, people make paper cranes in memory of Sadako's bravery.

Fundraiser

Christopher Reeve (1952–2004)

Christopher Reeve became **famous** for acting in the Superman movies. But in 1995 Reeve fell from his horse and was badly injured. His arms and legs were paralyzed. For the rest of his life, he needed a wheelchair.

Reeve decided to put his fame to good use. He spent the rest of his life raising money to help others who were paralyzed.

"You've got to give more than you take."

Reeve died in 2004. He will always be remembered as Superman. But he will also be remembered as someone who did a lot of good for people with disabilities.

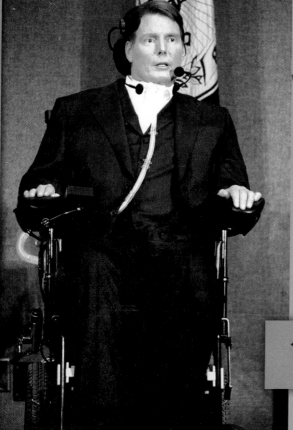

◄ Christopher Reeve spoke to many audiences.

CHAPTER 4

What Makes a Hero?

In this book you have read about many different people. Some have set out on a mission and shown great courage. Some have used their amazing strength to help those in need. Others have worked with perseverance to make their world a better place.

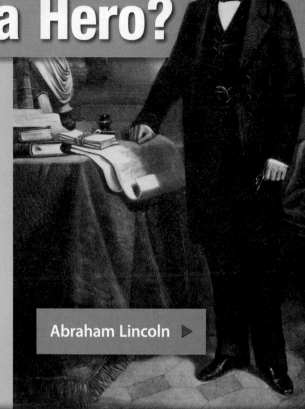

Abraham Lincoln ▶

◀ Roberto Clemente

People have different ideas about the qualities that make someone a hero. What do you think? There are some ideas about heroic qualities in the chart below. Can you think of others?

Now turn the page and read about Jenny Potts and Seth Hillman. Do you think either one has the qualities of a hero? What do their actions tell you about them?

◀ Hua Mulan

Heroes might

- show great courage.
- use their strength to help others.
- work quietly at tasks they believe in.
- keep going when things get hard.
- take risks for people they don't know.

Susie King Taylor ▶

News - Gazette

Whales high and dry

Stranded whales have become a big problem at Dungeness Spit in Washington state. Yesterday, biologist Jenny Potts and her team were called to help yet another orca stranded on the beach.

"There have been many strandings this season," Potts said. "It's hard work moving a whale back to the open ocean, but that's what we're paid to do."

Potts and her team got the latest orca back into the water at noon, but the whale soon beached itself again.

"We were disappointed, but we just got on with the job," said one worker.

This morning the team used a sling to tow the orca away from the shore.

"When we let him go, he finally swam in the right direction," said Potts. "The best thing about this job is seeing whales swim home."

An orca whale, like the ones shown swimming as a pod in this picture, was stranded yesterday at Dungeness Spit.

Marcela's Blog

Friday, August 10

I just read about a boy called Seth Hillman. When he was ten, Seth found out he had cancer. He was scared, but he wanted to stay positive so that he could help other kids like himself.

Seth decided to start a band. He soon had six band members—all kids with cancer, like himself. They called themselves the Storm Petrels. Since then, they've played at lots of fundraising events for kids with cancer.

Seth gets stage fright, but he says it's worth it. He says, "Keeping your spirits up is a big part of living with cancer. I know we're making a difference."

Listen to the Storm Petrels

Posted by Marcela at 2:18 p.m.

Sum It Up

Some people think a hero is strong and has courage. Other people think a hero is loyal and determined.

Whatever the qualities of a hero are, one thing is certain: The actions of a hero make a positive difference to one person or to many people's lives.

What qualities do you think a hero should have?

What kind of hero could you be?

The Hunter

A Chinese folktale
retold by Mary Casanova

Illustrations by Ed Young

The author first heard this story
from an exchange student from Chang
Chun, the capital city in the Ji Lin
province of northeast China. The tale
that was shared may be found in
Zhongguo Tonghua (Chinese Fairy Tales)
under the title *Lieh Ren Hai Li Bu (The
Hunter Hai Li Bu)*, edited by Zheng Shuo
Ren and Gu Nai Qing and published by
Shang Hai Wen Yi.

Contents

ONCE, IN A TINY CHINESE VILLAGE wedged between mountains and sea, lived a young hunter named Hai Li Bu. Though Hai Li Bu was a good hunter, providing fresh fish and meat for the villagers as best he could, a drought came. Day after dry day, the sun scorched the countryside and burned the villagers' crops. Soon there wasn't enough food to go around. The children rarely laughed, the young women seldom sang, and the white-haired people were too weak to leave their mats. Worst of all, the villagers began to argue and stopped listening to one another.

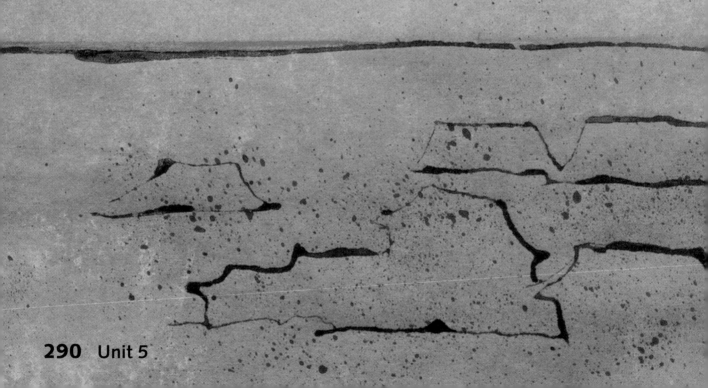

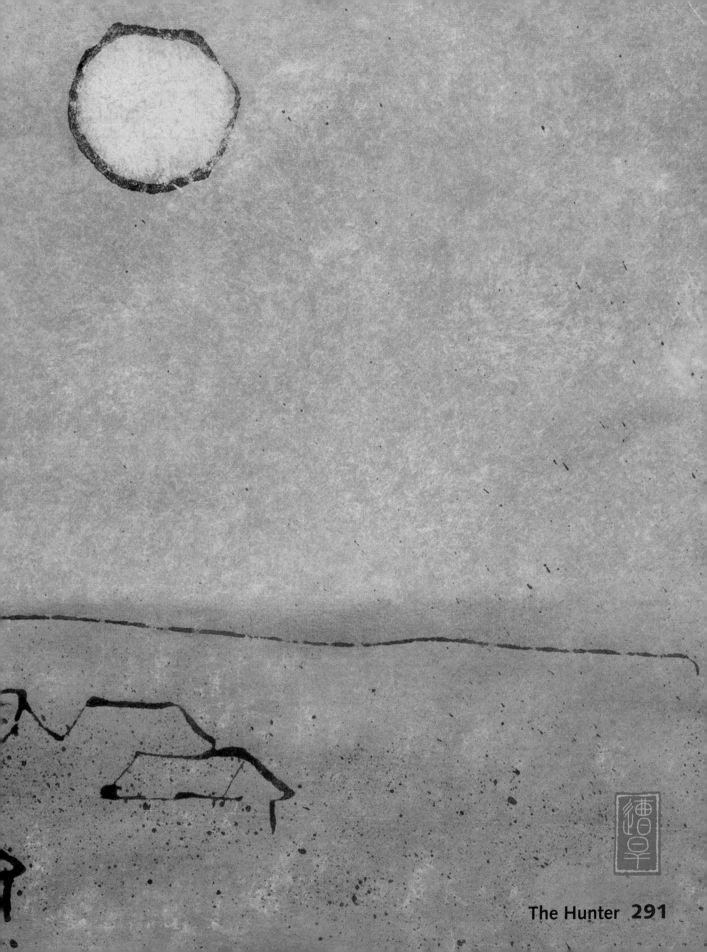

With each passing day, Hai Li Bu hunted deeper and deeper into the forest, desperately searching for game. One day, he spotted a small, pearly snake warming itself on a rock. Not wanting to **disturb** the snake's sleep, Hai Li Bu stepped softly around it on the withered grass.

Suddenly, a crane dropped from the clouds. Flapping its long gray wings, it snatched up the pearly snake and climbed high into the sky.

"Help me!" the little snake cried.

What? thought Hai Li Bu. The snake can speak?

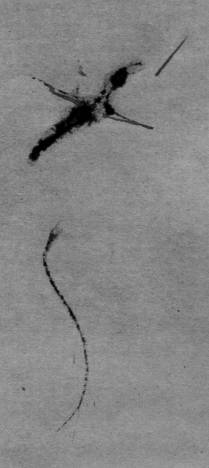

With a whisper, the hunter's arrow flew—
whoosh!—and though it missed the crane by
a feather, the bird squawked and released its
hold. The little snake dropped to the forest
floor and silently slithered away.

The Hunter 295

The next day, when Hai Li Bu returned to the forest, the little snake approached him on the path.

"My father, the Dragon King of the Sea," she said, "wants to thank you for saving my life. Will you come?"

Though Hai Li Bu needed to hunt, he didn't want to offend the snake. "Of course," he replied, and followed her down a winding path to a crystal palace beneath the sea.

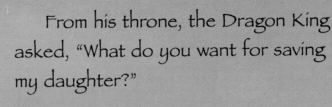

From his throne, the Dragon King asked, "What do you want for saving my daughter?"

Hai Li Bu shrugged his broad shoulders. "What more could I need, except to better provide for my village?"

The Dragon King showed Hai Li Bu his thousand and seventy treasures: sparkling red rubies, forest green emeralds, ocean blue sapphires, and shimmery pink pearls. "I will give you anything," he said.

"Your treasures are beautiful," the hunter answered, "but the only thing I desire is to understand the language of animals. Then I can be a better hunter."

The Dragon King reared back and from out of his mouth shot a round stone. "Take it," he said, "and your wish will come true. But remember one thing: You must not pass on the secret of your gift, or you will surely turn to stone, like the one you now hold."

With the stone in his leather pouch, Hai Li Bu hurried back to the forest. From the chatter of finches he learned where mountain goats wandered and where wild boar bedded down. He learned of shallows where fish were plentiful and where clams clustered in the sand. Each day, Hai Li Bu returned to his parched village with an even greater offering of food. Soon, the village was filled with laughter. The children's cheeks grew round and soft. The white-haired people left their mats to share their stories. The young women sang songs and whispered about who Hai Li Bu would someday marry.

But one dawn, the forest was unusually full with the chatter of birds and animals.

"Lightning and heavy rains are coming," cried the foxes. "The entire village will be flooded!"

"Tomorrow," the bears bellowed, "the mountaintop will crumble to the sea!"

"Who knows," the birds called, "how many people will die!"

Hai Li Bu's mouth went dry as the drought. He dropped his bow to the ground and rushed back to his village to warn his people.

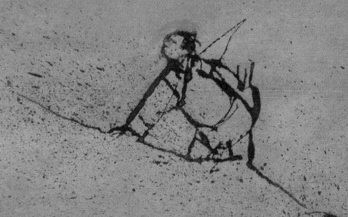

"Listen!" he shouted. "We must leave! The village will be destroyed!"

The villagers gathered around him, looking sideways at Hai Li Bu.

"Maybe he's been in the woods too long," said a young woman.

"Maybe he needs a rest," said a white-haired man.

"Maybe he's joking," said a child.

"Please," begged Hai Li Bu, "you must listen and believe me!"

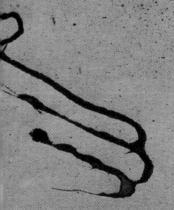
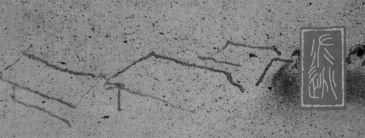

A village elder stepped forward. "Where did you learn this terrible news?"

Hai Li Bu suddenly remembered the Dragon King's warning.

He whispered, "Do you want me to die so you can believe?"

"Of course not," the elder said. He squared his arms and gestured to the simple huts. "But you ask us to leave our homes. How can we know what you say is true?"

Hai Li Bu stroked his chin. What should he do? If they wouldn't listen, should he flee and save himself? The villagers pressed closer. Like the wind that began to stir the treetops, they whispered among themselves.

How could he make them listen? He reached into his pouch and in his palm held out the round, luminous stone. But the villagers looked blankly at the stone and at Hai Li Bu.

The hunter sighed. He studied the villagers' faces—young and old—more splendid than jewels. No. Of course, he could never allow them to be destroyed.

Raindrops began to fall—*plink, plink, plink*—
on the dusty street.

Hai Li Bu drew a deep breath. He told of the little snake and the Dragon King's gift. Then he pointed to the inky line of birds flying south. "Look," he said, "the birds flee." As he spoke, his toes grew stiff as stones. "Tomorrow the mountain will be struck by lightning," he added, and his legs became granite hard. "The village will be flooded," he said, and his hands stopped in midair. "Listen," he said, "believe me and have courage." And as he spoke these last words, his lips turned to stone.

The Hunter 313

The villagers were stunned. They threw themselves at Hai Li Bu's feet and wept. As the rain grew heavier, the villagers ran to their houses, packed what they could carry on their backs, and fled.

The next day, as the animals had warned, thunder rattled the countryside. Lightning cracked the mountain peak, and boulders crashed into the valley below. Raindrops fell in sheets and washed the valley, utterly destroying the tiny village.

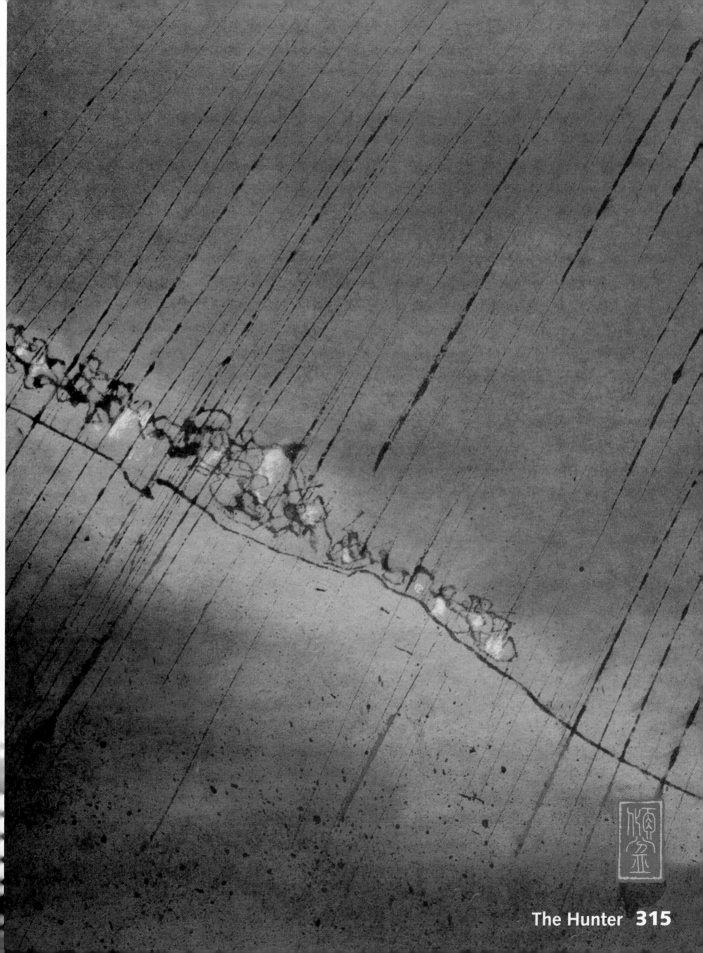

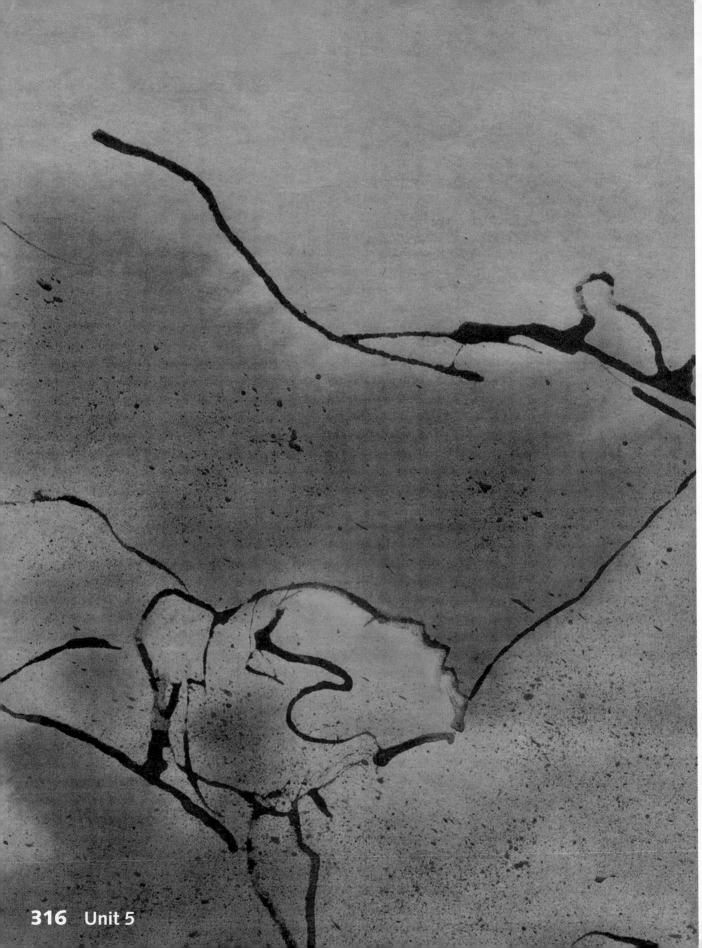

Days passed, and the people returned. But before rebuilding their village, they searched for Hai Li Bu in his stone prison. They found him, half-buried in the mud, and gently, gently, with many hands and many tears, carried him to what remained of the top of the mountain.

"If only we had not doubted him," the people said. "If only we'd listened."

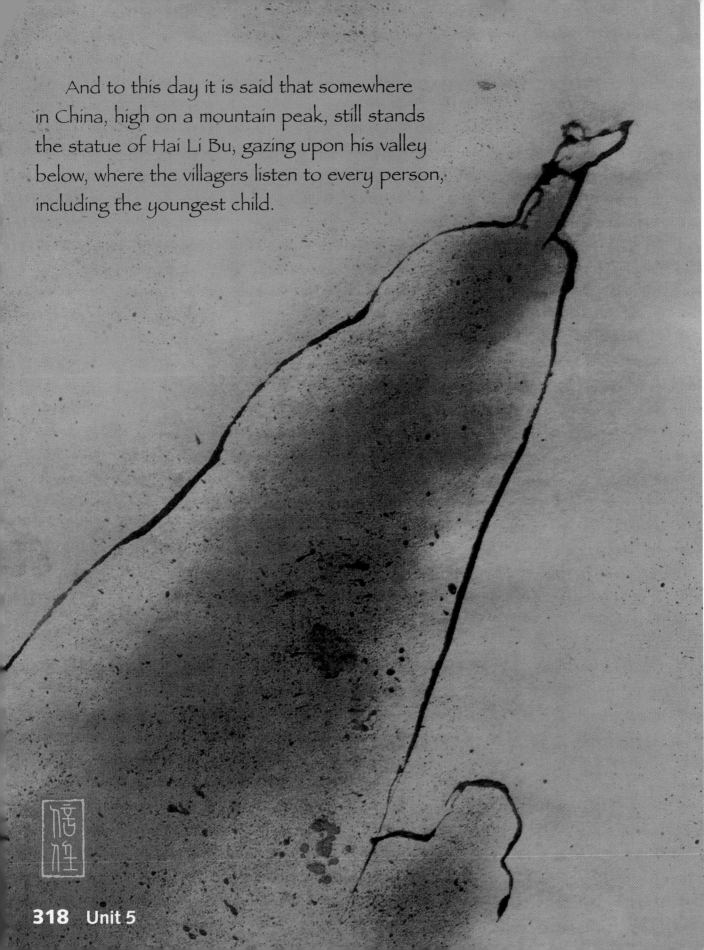

And to this day it is said that somewhere in China, high on a mountain peak, still stands the statue of Hai Li Bu, gazing upon his valley below, where the villagers listen to every person, including the youngest child.

Extreme Environments

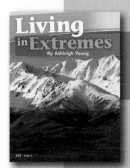

THEME Question

What does it take to survive in the wild?

Focus Questions

What makes an environment extreme?

How do living things survive in extreme environments?

Why do some living things have extreme features?

How do living things react to extreme changes in their environment?

Living
in Extremes
by Ashleigh Young

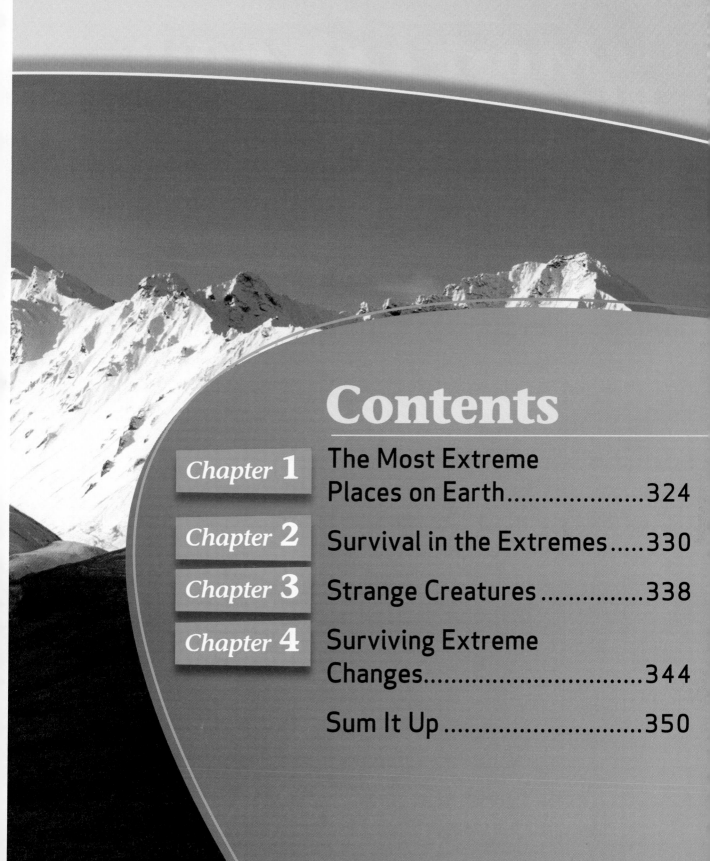

Contents

CHAPTER 1

The Most Extreme Places on Earth

Imagine you live in the hottest place on Earth. It hardly ever rains. You are always thirsty. Or maybe you live in the coldest place on Earth. You need to wear five layers of clothing just to take a walk!

Incredible places like these are known as extreme environments. All plants and animals need food, water, air, and shelter. These things may be hard to find in extreme environments.

The place where one type of plant or animal lives is called its **habitat**. Several different living things can share the same habitat. For example, frogs and flies will live in the same pond.

A biome is bigger than a habitat. It can include many different habitats. It also has its own climate, such as hot, rainy, or freezing cold!

Arctic biome

alpine biome

Tundra

The Arctic tundra is a cold biome near the North Pole. The soil in the tundra is almost always frozen.

Alpine

Alpine biomes are found just below the snowline in high mountain areas. The soil is rocky and dry.

Hot and Cold

Life must be hard for emperor penguins. After all, they live in Antarctica. That is the coldest place on Earth! Luckily, emperor penguins have lots of fat and a thick coat of feathers. These things help them keep warm, even when a blizzard is blowing snow around.

Antarctica surrounds the South Pole. It is the coldest, windiest place on Earth.

The Sonoran Desert covers 120,000 square miles of southwestern Arizona and southeastern California.

Kangaroo rats have an extreme home too. It is the Sonoran Desert of Arizona and California. A desert is a place where it doesn't often rain. But kangaroo rats don't need to drink water. They get all the water they need from the tiny seeds that they eat.

Believe it or not, Antarctica is a desert too. Almost no rain falls there. All deserts are extreme environments. Only the toughest plants and animals can survive there.

kangaroo rat

Deep and Dark

Imagine traveling in a submarine to the deepest part of the ocean. Soon it gets very dark and cold. You might think that nothing could survive in such a deep, dark place. Well, you would be wrong! When you turn on the searchlight, you might see all kinds of strange creatures—a glowing squid, an eel with a mouth bigger than its body, or a gigantic crab!

The deep sea hatchetfish lives in a world without much sunlight.

A special underwater craft can dive deep to where this giant spider crab lives.

The deepest part of the world's ocean is the Mariana Trench in the Pacific Ocean. The deep ocean is an extreme habitat. Very few plants are able to grow there because there is no sunlight. Without plants, sea creatures don't have much food to eat. These creatures must eat food that has fallen from above or eat each other!

Mariana Trench
36,198 ft. deep

Empire State Building
1,250 ft. high

CHAPTER 2

Survival in the Extremes

People need to take special clothing or equipment to survive when they go into an extreme environment, such as a desert. Plants and animals don't need to do that! The plants and animals in extreme environments have developed special features and behaviors. These features and behaviors are known as **adaptations**. They help the plants and animals find food and water, keep cool or warm, and stay safe from predators. A predator is an animal that hunts other animals for food.

This snake's scaly skin is an adaptation that helps to keep it from drying out.

An adaptation may be something that you can see, such as sharp, pointy spines on a plant. It may also be something that a living thing does, such as an animal hunting at night.

Camel Features

A camel has adapted for life in the desert. It has wide, flat feet for walking on sand and long eyelashes that keep dust and sand out of its eyes.

eyelashes

wide, flat feet

Little Water

All living things need water. Water is scarce in many extreme environments. Plants and animals that live in these environments have adaptations that help them get the water they need. Some desert plants like cacti have wide, shallow roots to suck up moisture from the ground. They store as much water as they can in their thick stems when it rains.

The darkling beetle has an unusual way of getting water too. It collects morning dew on its back!

cactus

Ribs along this cactus's stem expand to store water.

back

mouth

Drops of dew run down the darkling beetle's back into its mouth.

sand grouse

The sand grouse flies away from its desert home to get water for its chicks. It soaks its feathers in a pool and flies back to its nest. The young birds drink the water from its feathers.

Extreme Temperatures

Plants and animals have features or physical parts that help them survive in extreme temperatures. A thick, furry coat keeps animals such as polar bears warm. Whales and seals have a layer of fat, called blubber, to keep out the cold.

One desert animal uses its ears to keep cool! The fennec fox lives in the desert. It has big ears. Its ears help the fox to release body heat and keep cool.

seal

The yak lives in cold, alpine climates. Underneath its coat of long hair is another layer of soft, fine hair called down.

yak

A New Home

One way to survive an extreme change in climate is to **migrate**. Many kinds of birds migrate huge distances to places where it is warmer and there is more food.

Plants and animals also do things that help them survive in extreme temperatures. Some Antarctic animals, such as penguins, huddle in groups. By doing this they provide one another with shelter and warmth. At the hottest part of the day, some desert animals find shelter from the sun underground or in bushes.

This desert tortoise is in its burrow to keep out of the sun.

Staying Alive

quills

Plants and animals in extreme environments have different ways of defending themselves from predators. Some animals blend in with their surroundings. Their enemies can't see them easily. Porcupines have sharp spikes called quills that they use to defend themselves. Plants can defend themselves too. Some plants have tough thorns or spines that are difficult for animals to chew.

The spines on these cacti keep animals from eating the parts of the plants where water is stored.

cactus

Wild horses use their speed to run away from danger.

Some animals stay together to protect themselves from predators. They travel and feed in large groups.

In the western United States, the wild horses of the Great Basin Desert live in herds for safety. The lead mare guides the herd to a safe area when they are threatened. The lead stallion follows at the back to protect them.

CHAPTER 3
Strange Creatures

You have read about how plants and animals adapt to survive. Sometimes these adaptations can be strange and interesting.

A Light Trap

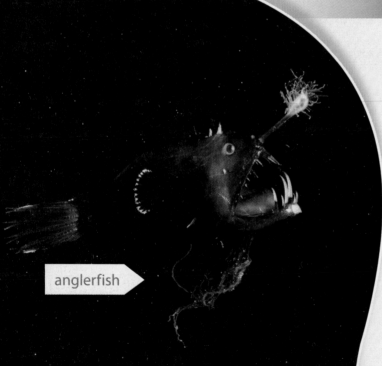

anglerfish

All living things need food. You have read that there isn't much to eat in the deepest parts of the ocean. Fish **compete** with one another for food scraps. Some fish have interesting ways of catching prey.

The female anglerfish dangles what appears to be a light over her head. The light looks like a fishing pole. It attracts smaller fish.

Living Rocks

Living rocks look very unusual, but they can be hard to see at first. They are small, fleshy plants that grow in the desert. Living rocks live up to their name: They look just like rocks! This adaptation keeps insects and animals from eating them.

Living rocks blend in with the stones and pebbles around them.

Hot Stuff

Nothing can survive in boiling water, right? Wrong! Thermophiles (*ther-mo-files*) can! Thermophiles are bacteria, very small living things, that have adapted to living in extremely hot places. These bacteria need hot temperatures to survive and grow. Some thermophiles live in volcanoes. Others live in hot springs.

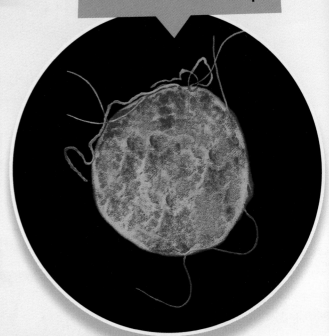

This is a thermophile as seen under a microscope.

Thermophiles help make the water in hot springs turn bright colors such as red, orange, and blue.

desert sand dune

Desert Dancer

The shovel-snouted lizard lives in the desert in Namibia, Africa. This lizard works hard to keep cool! It keeps two feet at a time off the hot sand. The lizard walks like this until the sand cools down. The lizard dives into the sand and wriggles down to a cooler level if it can't get cool on top.

The shovel-snouted lizard looks like it's dancing on the sand.

mountains

Mountain Plants

Mountains can be hard places to live. They are often cold, windy, and dry. Mountain plants need special ways of surviving in this harsh environment. Some plants grow in tight mats very close to the ground. This protects the plants from the strong winds that blow high up mountainsides.

Hairs that look like fuzzy white wool cover this plant and hold in heat.

Extreme environments often create extreme plants and animals. Their weird and wonderful features help them survive where others can't.

extremely hot

extremely quick

extremely deep

extremely shiny

CHAPTER 4

Surviving Extreme Changes

When an environment changes, it **affects** the plants and animals that live there. They may need to adapt to the change or find a new habitat if they are going to survive. Sometimes a change is fast. For example, a flood or fire sends animals rushing to safety. On the other hand a change can be slow but still extreme, such as pollution. Over time a small rise in temperature can change an environment and affect plants and animals.

When the temperature rises, ice in the North and South Poles melts.

ice

Survival may mean finding new kinds of food to eat. It may mean building a home in a different place. Plants may slow their growth. Or they may grow in a different place, such as the nooks and crannies of rocks. Some desert plants have adapted to the shifting sands of the desert. The soaptree yucca grows quickly to keep the sand dunes from burying it.

soaptree yucca

Some raccoons have learned to pull the lids off garbage cans.

City Animals

Each year towns and cities grow, and land is cleared to build new houses. Clearing land destroys the habitats of many animals. To survive they often come into urban areas looking for food.

Wildfire!

Thick smoke fills the air. There's a sound of crackling branches and leaves. It's a wildfire! In hot, dry places, a forest can go up in flames at the drop of a hat. Animals must react quickly in order to survive. They often have to move far from their habitat to escape the fire. In contrast some plants have adapted to the extreme heat of fires.

Fire breaks open and forces seeds to drop out of the cones of lodgepole pines.

fire

A flood can destroy animals' homes and sources of food.

Flash Flood!

Heavy rainfall can be dangerous to living things. Animals must flee to higher ground or move inland as water rises. Birds that nest on the ground, such as pheasants and quail, must rebuild their nests after a flood.

Rising water forces deer to move to higher ground.

A Changing Climate

The climate of Earth is slowly changing. Temperatures are rising in many parts of the world. Some animals are moving to cooler places as a result.

Plants and animals are changing their behaviors too. Plants flower and birds migrate earlier when warm spring weather comes earlier.

White storks are building their nests higher up the mountain where it is cooler.

nest

Breaking the Food Chain

Every living thing is part of a **food chain**. A food chain is a group of living things that need one another for food. Each living thing is a "link" in the food chain. If something happens to one of the links, it can break the chain. Then some animals might struggle to find enough to eat. Some living things might increase in number.

The horned lizard is part of a desert food chain. It eats mostly ants. Ants feed on the seeds of mesquite bushes. They might not have enough food if the mesquite bushes should disappear. The ants might die or move away. Then the horned lizard might have to find food somewhere else. The food chain below shows how these living things are connected.

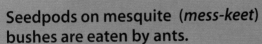
Ants are eaten by horned lizards.

Seedpods on mesquite (*mess-keet*) bushes are eaten by ants.

Horned lizards are eaten by hawks.

Sum It Up

Earth is made up of many biomes. Some biomes are freezing cold. Other biomes are boiling hot. Still others are dark as night. Yet plants and animals live in all the different biomes. They have developed special features and ways of behaving that help them to survive in these extreme environments.

We share planet Earth with all kinds of unusual living things. Learning about them helps us to understand how extraordinary our world is.

polar bear

HOTTEST COLDEST HIGHEST DEEPEST

STEVE JENKINS

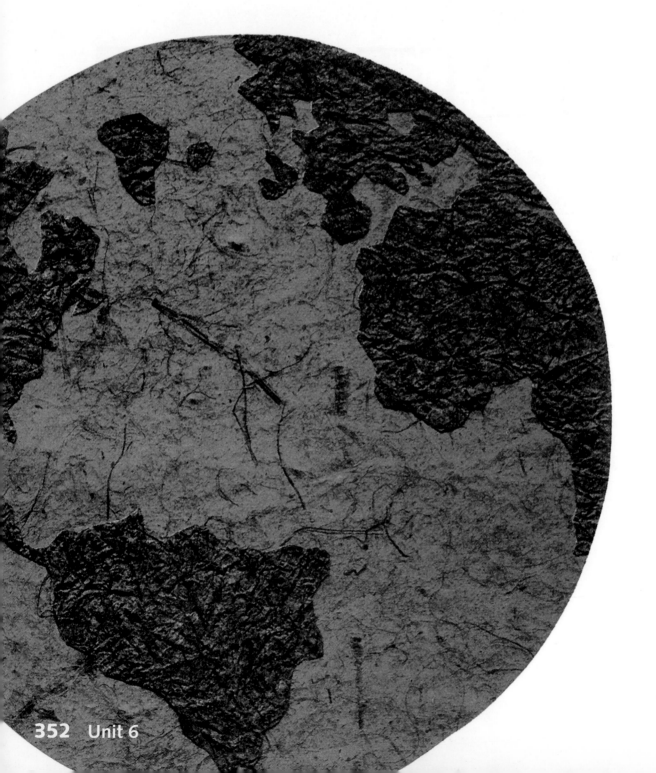

If you could visit any spot on earth, where would you go? What if you wanted to see some of the most amazing natural wonders in the world?

There are deserts that haven't seen rain for hundreds of years and jungles where it pours almost every day. There are places so cold that even in the summer it's below freezing and spots where it's often hot enough to cook an egg on the ground. There are mountains many miles high and ocean trenches that are even deeper. You can find rivers thousands of miles long and waterfalls thousands of feet high.

Where are the very hottest and coldest, windiest and snowiest, highest and deepest places on earth? **Travel** the world and visit the planet's record holders.

United States
(2,750 miles wide)

Nile River (4,145 miles)

Amazon River (4,007 miles)

Chiang Jiang (3,964 miles)

Mississippi-Missouri (3,710 miles)

LIBYA

EGYPT

SAUDI ARABIA

CHAD

NILE RIVER

RED SEA

SUDAN

ETHIOPIA

The Nile, in Africa, is the longest river
in the world. It is 4,145 miles long.

The Amazon River, in South America, is not as long—4,007 miles—but it is considered mightier because it **carries** half of all the river water in the world. The Chiang Jiang (Yangtze), in Asia (3,964 miles), and the Mississippi–Missouri, in the United States (3,710 miles), are the world's third and fourth longest rivers.

Lake Baikal, in Russia, is the world's oldest
and deepest lake. The lake was formed
about 25 million years ago. In one spot it is
5,134 feet deep.

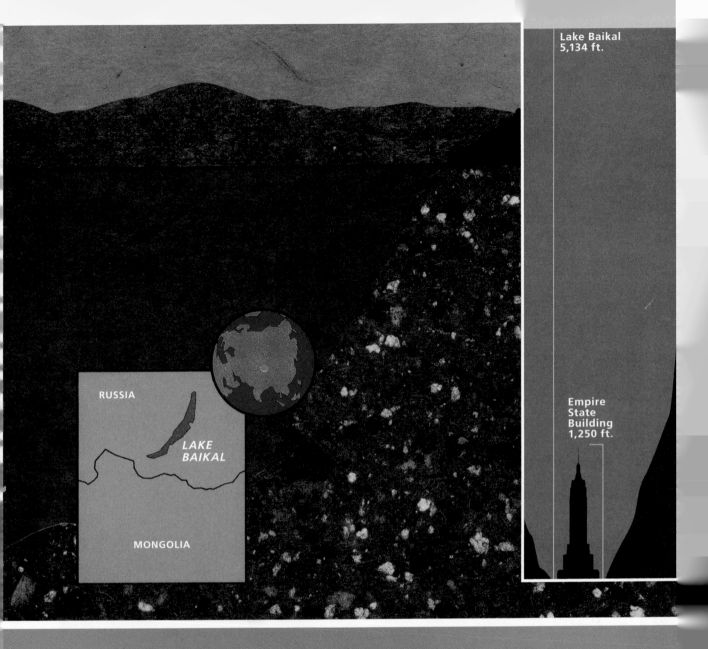

Lake Baikal
5,134 ft.

Empire
State
Building
1,250 ft.

RUSSIA

LAKE
BAIKAL

MONGOLIA

The largest freshwater lake in the world is
Lake Superior, one of the Great Lakes in North
America (31,700 square miles), but Lake Baikal
(5,500 square miles) contains more water than
any other lake on earth—more than all five
Great Lakes combined.

Mount Everest is the highest mountain in the world. Its peak is 29,028 feet above sea level.

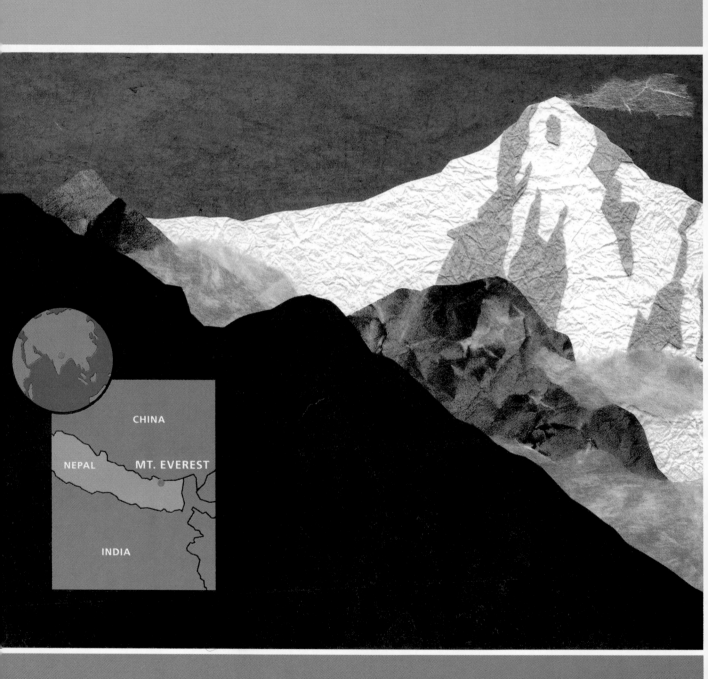

CHINA

NEPAL   MT. EVEREST

INDIA

The highest mountain in North America is Mount McKinley (also called Denali), in Alaska, at 20,320 feet. Mount Whitney, in California, is the highest peak in the continental United States. Its summit is 14,491 feet above sea level.

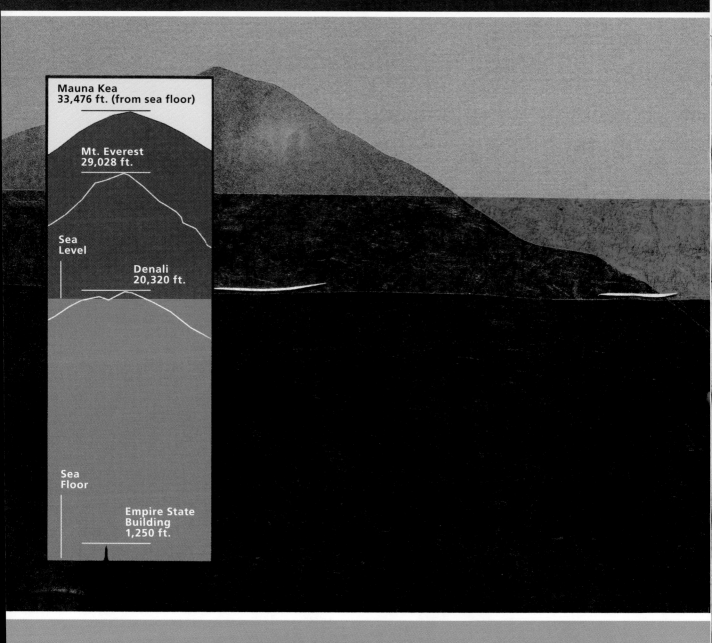

Mauna Kea
33,476 ft. (from sea floor)

Mt. Everest
29,028 ft.

Sea
Level

Denali
20,320 ft.

Sea
Floor

Empire State
Building
1,250 ft.

Mount Everest is considered the highest
mountain—above sea level—in the world, but
it's not really the tallest. Measured from its base
on the floor of the ocean, Mauna Kea, in Hawaii,
is 33,476 feet tall. Only the top 13,796 feet of
Mauna Kea are above sea level.

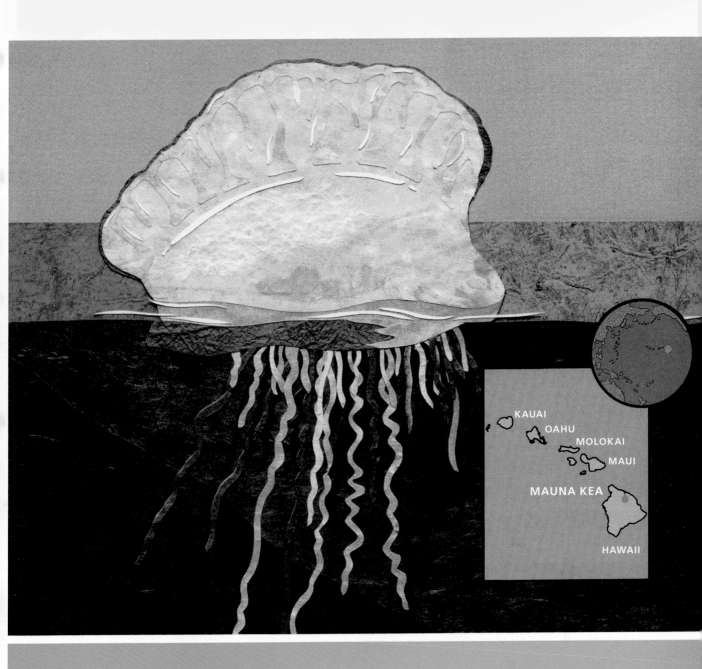

Mount Everest rises from a plateau that is already 17,000 feet above sea level, so one would have to climb only about 12,000 feet to reach its summit. Mount McKinley, in Alaska, is almost 20,000 feet from base to summit.

The hottest spot on the planet is Al Aziziyah,
Libya, in the Sahara, where a temperature of
over 136° F has been recorded.

136°F
134.6°F

98.6°F
Body
temp.

68°F
Room
temp.

32°F
Water
freezes

The hottest temperature ever recorded in the
United States is 134.6° F in Death Valley, California.

The coldest place on the planet is Vostok, Antarctica. A temperature of 129° F below zero was recorded there.

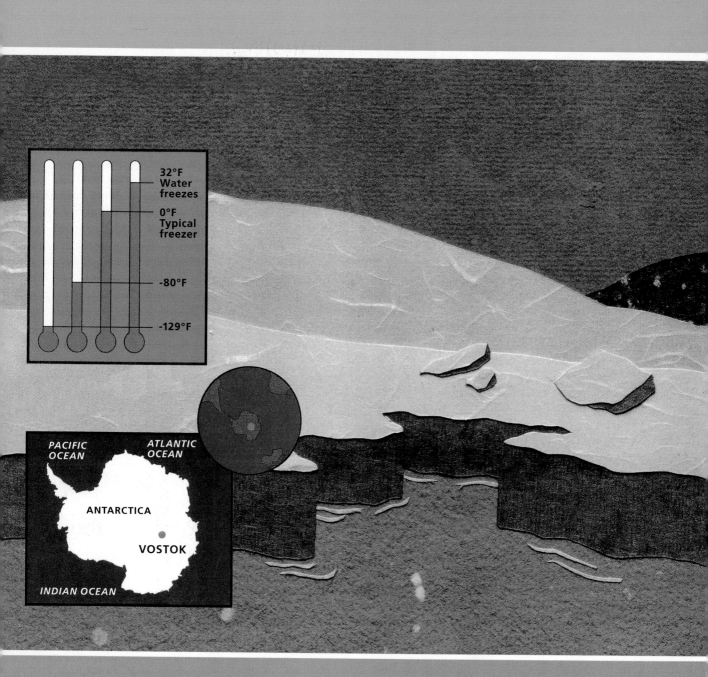

32°F
Water
freezes

0°F
Typical
freezer

-80°F

-129°F

PACIFIC
OCEAN

ATLANTIC
OCEAN

ANTARCTICA

VOSTOK

INDIAN OCEAN

It is so cold at the South Pole that the average summer temperature is -58° F. The coldest temperature ever recorded in the United States is -80° F, at Prospect Creek Camp, Alaska.

The wettest place on earth is Tutunendo, Colombia, where an average of 463 inches of rain falls every year.

463 in.
Tutunendo
average
annual
precipitation

36 in.
Chicago
average
annual
precipitation

61 in.
La Réunion
one day rainfall

72 in.
Adult Man

Mount Wai-ale-ale, on the island of Kauai in
Hawaii, has the most rainy days—350 a year.
On the island of La Réunion, in the Indian Ocean,
more than 61 inches of rain fell in a single day.

The driest place is the Atacama Desert, in Chile, where no rain has fallen for the last 400 years.

72 in.
Adult Man

10 in.
Desert
precipitation

1½ in.
Death Valley
average annual
precipitation

Any place that receives less than 10 inches of precipitation a year is considered a desert. The driest place in the United States is Death Valley, California, where only about 1½ inches of rain falls every year.

The windiest spot on earth is atop Mount Washington, in New Hampshire. A wind speed of 231 miles per hour has been recorded there.

10 mph
Breezy Day

150 mph
Severe Hurricane

231 mph
Mt. Washington

It is also very windy near the tops of the world's
highest mountains, the Himalayas. Many of these
peaks are tall enough to reach the jet stream,
a narrow, strong air current that is found above
28,000 feet.

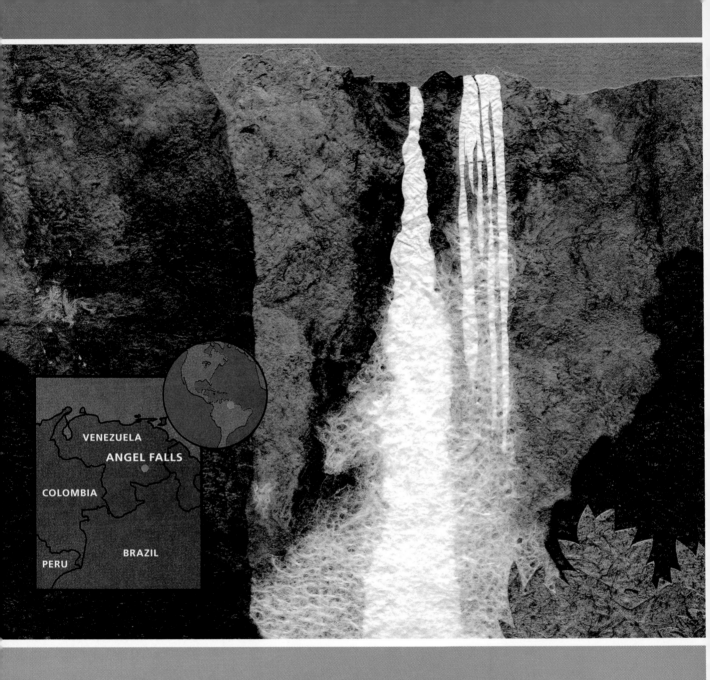

The world's highest waterfall is Angel Falls, in Venezuela. It is 3,212 feet high.

Angel Falls is more than seventeen times higher
than Niagara Falls (180 feet), in New York State.
Victoria Falls in Zimbabwe, Africa, carries more
water than any other waterfall. It is 355 feet high.

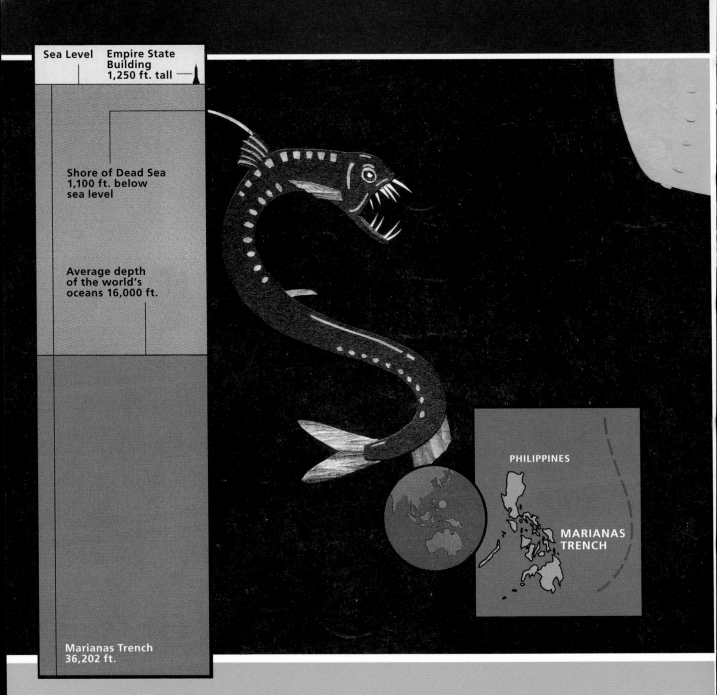

Sea Level   **Empire State Building** 1,250 ft. tall

Shore of Dead Sea 1,100 ft. below sea level

Average depth of the world's oceans 16,000 ft.

PHILIPPINES

MARIANAS TRENCH

Marianas Trench 36,202 ft.

The deepest spot in the ocean is the Marianas Trench, in the Philippines. It is 36,202 feet deep.

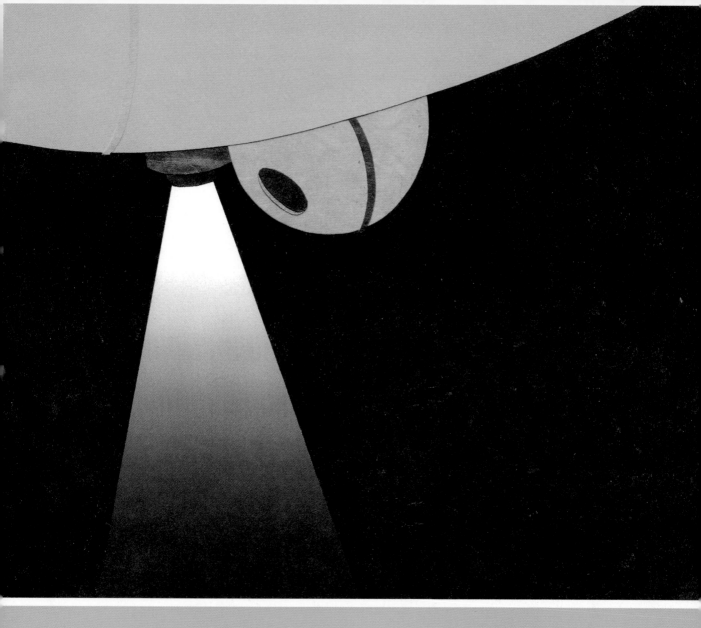

The average depth of the world's oceans is about 3 miles, or 16,000 feet. The lowest spot on dry land is the shore of the Dead Sea, 1,100 feet below sea level.

The world's most active volcano is Sangay, in Ecuador. Since 1937, it has erupted once every 24 hours on average. It once erupted more than 400 times in a single day.

Etna
3,500 years

How long have
these volcanoes
been erupting?

Aso
1,460 years

Colima
437 years

Sangay
60 years

Other very active volcanoes include Colima,
in Mexico (it has erupted regularly since 1560);
Aso, in Japan (erupting since 533); and Mount Etna,
in Italy (erupting regularly since 1500 B.C.).

The most extreme tides occur in the Bay of Fundy, in Nova Scotia, Canada. There the water level rises and falls more than 50 feet every 6 hours.

MAINE

NOVA SCOTIA

BAY OF FUNDY

The tide here comes in so fast that it can overtake a person trying to outrun it.

54 ft.
Bay of Fundy

3 ft.
Typical East
Coast tide

6 ft.
Adult Man

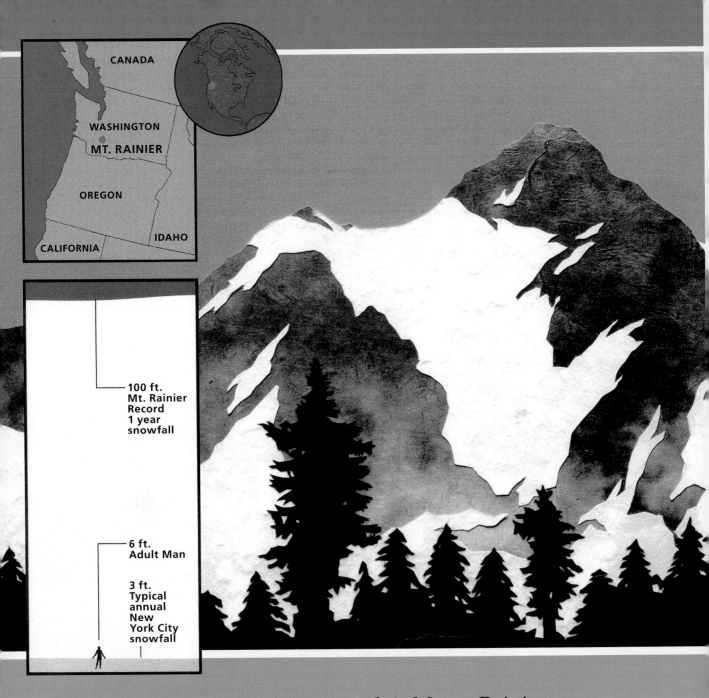

CANADA

WASHINGTON

MT. RAINIER

OREGON

IDAHO

CALIFORNIA

100 ft.
Mt. Rainier
Record
1 year
snowfall

6 ft.
Adult Man

3 ft.
Typical
annual
New
York City
snowfall

The snowiest place on earth is Mount Rainier,
in Washington State. One year, more than
1,200 inches of snow fell there.

Mount Rainier is covered in snow the whole year.
Some of the snow has formed glaciers, masses of
ice that slowly move down the mountain under
their own weight.

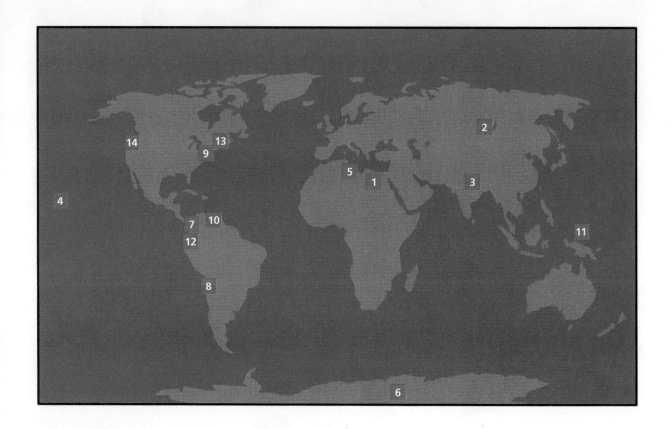

1. Nile River, Africa
2. Lake Baikal, Russia
3. Mount Everest, Nepal
4. Mauna Kea, Hawaii
5. Al Aziziyah, Libya
6. Vostok, Antarctica
7. Tutunendo, Colombia
8. Atacama Desert, Chile
9. Mount Washington, New Hampshire
10. Angel Falls, Venezuela
11. Marianas Trench, Philippines
12. Sangay, Ecuador
13. Bay of Fundy, Nova Scotia
14. Mount Rainier, Washington

UNIT 7

Making a Difference

In what ways do people make a difference?

p. 384

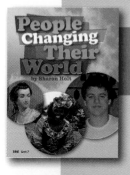

People Changing Their World
Nonfiction: Informational Text

p. 386

Fishing Day *Fiction: Historical Fiction*

p. 415

THEME
Question

In what ways do people make a difference?

Focus Questions

How have people in the past changed our lives today?

How can people change their community?

How do ordinary people make a difference every day?

How do we turn ideas into actions to make a difference?

People Changing Their World

by Sharon Holt

Chapter 1

The Freedom Makers

In the United States we're free to do many things. We're free to turn on the radio and find out what's happening in the world. We're free to pick up a book and read about the lives of other people. But many people in other countries are not allowed to choose what to watch or read. Their leaders decide for them.

In the United States people are free to read what they like.

Many people have worked hard to give us the **freedom** and **rights** we have today. For example, the Founding Fathers realized that freedom won't happen unless you take action. These leaders fought the Revolutionary War because they felt strongly that our country should be free from British rule. When the war was over, the Founding Fathers wrote the Constitution of the United States of America to protect the freedom and rights of all U.S. citizens.

Abigail Adams made a big difference to the United States in the late 1700s.

Abigail Adams— First Lady

Abigail Adams was the wife of the Founding Father and second President of the United States, John Adams.

In 1775 the Massachusetts Colony General Court asked Mrs. Adams to speak to women about the U.S. movement toward independence.

Abigail Adams supported equal rights for women and called for better schooling for girls.

Like her husband, she also opposed slavery.

The Civil Rights Movement

Over time people made changes to the Constitution that our Founding Fathers wrote. They also passed new laws. These changes and laws gave the same rights to all Americans. It hasn't always been easy to make those changes.

Some people who fought hard for change took part in the Civil Rights Movement. They saw that African American people didn't have the same freedom as white people. They wanted all Americans to be treated as equals.

Activists like Dr. Martin Luther King, Jr., held rallies to speak to people about the rights of African Americans.

People gather to join a civil rights march in Florida.

Before 1954 most African American children didn't go to the same schools as white children. In many parts of the United States, African Americans were allowed to sit only at the back of buses. They weren't even allowed to eat in some diners. The goal of the Civil Rights Movement was to give African American people the same rights as white people.

Ruby Bridges

In 1960 Ruby Bridges was one of the first African American children to go to the same school as white children. Some people protested against African American children going to the same schools as white children.

Rights for Women and Children

Another group that fought for change was the National American Woman Suffrage Association.

At school we may vote for our class president. It is like voting for the U.S. President. All U.S. citizens are allowed to vote after they are 18 years old. But there was a time when only men were allowed to vote.

The National American Woman Suffrage Association was formed in 1890 to fight for women to be allowed to vote too. They worked hard to reach their goal. In 1920 the Constitution was changed to give women the right to vote.

This photo, taken in 1913, shows members of the National American Woman Suffrage Association in Washington, D.C.

In the early 1900s many children worked in factories.

The National Child Labor Committee began in 1904. In those days many children did not go to school. Instead they had to work all day for very little pay. This angered the people on the committee. They fought to change the Constitution.

In 1938 a law was passed that said that children are not allowed to work in most jobs until they are fourteen years old. The law also limits the number of hours children are allowed to work.

Chapter 2

Every Person Counts

Many people worked together to improve the Constitution. They also changed certain laws in order to limit child labor. Sometimes a small group of people or just one person can make big changes.

It can be easy to make a change if we feel strongly about something. By doing something that we **believe** in, we can all make a difference in our community.

mural

Students work together to paint a mural for their town.

People Who Make a Difference

Mimi Ausland of Bend, Oregon, has always loved animals. When she was twelve years old, she made a Web site. Her Web site was started to help feed dogs at her local animal shelter.

Every day the Web site asks a different question about dogs. Whenever someone answers a question, a business gives free dog food to the animal shelter. Mimi has also started the same kind of Web site for cats.

Mimi holds one of the dogs she has helped at the animal shelter in Bend, Oregon.

Sisters Robin and Starla Krause teach at Loring Elementary School in Minneapolis, Minnesota. In 2003 they started an after-school cooking class to help children learn about eating food that is healthful. They called it Kids Cook.

Now the students are also growing a school garden. They plant fruit and vegetables in their garden, harvest the food, and use it to make meals that are healthful.

Starla
Krause

Robin
Krause

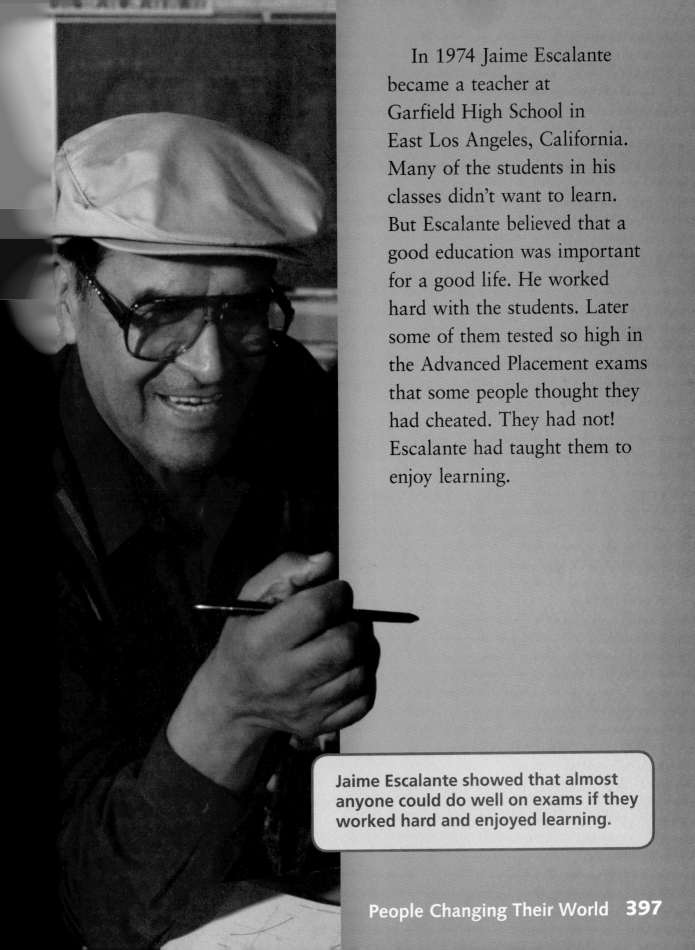

In 1974 Jaime Escalante became a teacher at Garfield High School in East Los Angeles, California. Many of the students in his classes didn't want to learn. But Escalante believed that a good education was important for a good life. He worked hard with the students. Later some of them tested so high in the Advanced Placement exams that some people thought they had cheated. They had not! Escalante had taught them to enjoy learning.

Jaime Escalante showed that almost anyone could do well on exams if they worked hard and enjoyed learning.

In 1982 six students from Texas A&M University started The BIG Event. They wanted to choose one day every year to thank their community for its support.

During The BIG Event students do jobs around the community. Many other universities and some high schools across the United States now give back to their communities just like the students at Texas A&M University do.

An event similar to The BIG Event is held each year in Miami, Florida. These students are improving their community by landscaping.

So what made these people give up their time to help others?

Mimi Ausland gave up her time because she loves animals. She wanted to help them and the people who care for them.

The Krauses wanted to help children be healthier. They decided to teach children about making good choices about food.

Jaime Escalante wanted his students to do well.

And the students from Texas A&M University wanted to thank their community for helping them.

Chapter 3

Everyday Change Makers

You don't have to be famous to change things. You don't have to be powerful either. Many of the ordinary people you see every day are making a difference in your community.

They might help serve food to people who are hungry, or they might plant trees. In big ways and small ways, ordinary people, leading regular lives, can help a community become better.

Planting a tree can make a difference to your community.

choir leader

This choir leader is giving her time for free.

People who do things without pay are called **volunteers**. Volunteers are important. When other people see how much fun it is to help, they want to take part too. Then they discover that it can be easy to make a difference.

Real Lifesavers

Some of the ordinary people who volunteer in our communities are real lifesavers. For example, some firefighters are volunteers. They don't get paid for working as firefighters. They give their time to make the community safer for everyone. They want to make a difference.

firefighter

lifeguard

Some firefighters and lifeguards work for no pay so they can keep their community safe.

Some people work to improve education in their communities. The children might need help with their homework, but their parents are busy. These volunteers run free homework centers.

Some people want their communities to be more fun and friendly. They plan events like street parties to help people meet one another and enjoy themselves.

All these volunteers see that their communities need something, and they think of a way to solve a problem. Then they look for other people who can help them make their ideas work.

This grandparent volunteers at a homework center in New York City.

Others like to help the people they know. They care for their friends' children when their friends are busy. They visit older people who need help. Or they help at their neighborhood school or community group.

All kinds of people help in different ways to change their communities. They turn something their community needs into the chance to meet other people, learn new things, and have fun.

These people are helping out at a shelter for the homeless.

Here are some small things that you can do to change your world.

You can work with your community to **organize** activities. Maybe the people in your neighborhood want to clean up trash in the area. Or a local organization can serve as a site for a canned food drive or a toy drive.

Every community has its own problems. They are just waiting for people to think of good ways of solving them.

Recycling your household trash makes a difference to your community.

Community Action Network

The Los Angeles Community Action Network (LA CAN) works to improve the community. How? Its members help people find good homes to live in, they take care of people who are sick, and they help people find jobs.

Peter White of LA CAN helps members of his community find solutions to problems.

Chapter 4

Do Something!

If you could do something to make a difference in this world, what would you do? Every change begins with an idea. Maybe people in another country have lost things in a flood and need help. Or maybe you feel that your neighborhood could be cleaner.

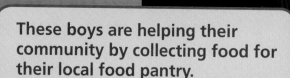

These boys are helping their community by collecting food for their local food pantry.

Once you have an idea, how do you make it happen? First, you need to make sure it's a good idea. Try asking other people what they think about your idea.

It's often easier to make an idea happen with some help. Ask other people to help you. When you have a team of helpers, you need to decide what to do.

A Decision-making Process

1. Figure out what the problem is.

2. List ideas that might solve the problem.

3. Compare the ideas and think about what is good and bad about each one.

4. Decide which idea is best.

5. Carry out the idea.

6. Figure out whether it was a good decision. Did it solve the problem?

Ideas That Solve Problems

As a teenager in New York City, New York, Avery Hairston had a good idea. He wanted to give energy-saving lightbulbs to low-income families. Energy-saving lightbulbs use less electricity. They also last longer than regular lightbulbs. However, they are more expensive to buy.

Avery asked his parents and friends to help him. Together, they started a charity to raise money to buy the lightbulbs. They called their charity RelightNY.

energy-saving lightbulb

Avery's idea has helped his community as well as the planet.

One of the RelightNY members hands out lightbulbs.

Avery had a simple idea, a team of helpers, and a plan. Now RelightNY has given thousands of energy-saving lightbulbs to people living all over New York City. And thousands of other people have heard about Avery's idea. They think it's a good idea. They are buying energy-saving lightbulbs too.

In 2005 Rajiv Kumar was living in Rhode Island. He was training to be a doctor. One of his teachers explained that more and more people were not eating healthful food and not getting enough exercise. Their lifestyles were bad for their health.

Kumar didn't like to think of people being unhealthy. He decided to do something about it. He started a competition to help people lose weight. He called his competition Shape Up RI. In this competition people work in teams to help one another eat the right kinds of food and exercise more.

Rajiv Kumar decided to do something to improve people's health in his community.

Kumar asked business owners to pay for their workers to join Shape Up RI. He was excited when 2,000 people joined up for the first Shape Up RI.

Shape Up RI now happens every year. It helps thousands of people feel better.

Many people have joined the Shape Up RI competition.

In the 1970s many people in Kenya were poor, and the land was eroding. Wangari Maathai came up with a great idea. The people could work planting trees to improve the land and give them wood for their cooking fires. Not only was Maathai keeping people from destroying forests in Kenya, she was also helping people to cook healthful food together. Maathai's idea became the Green Belt Movement.

Wangari Maathai has won the Nobel Peace Prize for her work.

Person/Group	What was the problem?	How was it solved?
Avery Hairston/ RelightNY	Not everyone in New York could afford energy-saving lightbulbs.	RelightNY gave energy-saving lightbulbs to needy people.
Rajiv Kumar/ Shape Up RI	Some people in Rhode Island had unhealthful lifestyles.	Shape Up RI improved people's exercise and diet habits.
Wangari Maathai/ Green Belt Movement	Kenya's environment was suffering.	The Green Belt Movement planted trees in Kenya.

Reflect on the actions of Rajiv Kumar, Avery Hairston, and Wangari Maathai. Then think about the things you could do to make a difference. Figure out how to explain your ideas to other people. Then choose a team to work with. Once you make a plan, you are well on your way!

These students and their teacher are planting flowers to make their school look nice.

Sum It Up

Remember the teacher Jaime Escalante? He changed the lives of the students in his classes because he wanted to make a difference in the world. You don't need to make a big change. But you can do something! Every change in history started with a person who had an idea. You could be one of those people. What you do right here, right now, can make a difference in the world.

ANDREA DAVIS PINKNEY

Fishing Day

Illustrated by
SHANE W. EVANS

When Saturday comes, Mama and I wake long before the sun, so we can catch the fish right when *they* wake.

"Mama, you up?" I call. But before Mama even answers, I smell hominy cooking in the kitchen.

Mama leans in the doorway of my bedroom. "I *been* up," she says. "Making sure we got us a hot breakfast."

I pull on my overalls and buckle them fast, before the cold has a chance to reach my bones.

In the kitchen, Mama says, "Eat good now, Reenie. We've got a long fishing day ahead."

Mama and me, we sure love fishing. We've got a special fishing place along the north bank of a wide muddy stream folks around here call Jim Crow River.

Mama baits each of our hooks with a kernel of corn from her sack, then casts the rest into the water. We watch the corn pellets float just below the water's surface. We wait for the carp to come along and nibble the tiny jewels of food.

Today the carp aren't taking up our bait.

"Not even a nibble," I say.

"Patience, Reenie," Mama says softly.

"Fish can be finicky at the start."

Suddenly a little stone skips across the water. Leaves crunch up behind us. It's Mr. Billy Troop and his boy, Pigeon. Pigeon's not his real true name. His real name is Peter. I call him Pigeon because when he and his daddy come to fish, Pigeon's doing everything but sitting still. He's always flitting somewhere. Just like an up-jumpy bird.

Mr. Troop's got his bucket of bait and two fishing rods. Pigeon races off toward the river's edge, skipping another stone, messing up the water's calm.

Mama shakes her head. "That boy's suffering from want," she says. "It's a shame, too, 'cause all of us—even the fish—suffer from the flurry he makes."

"A shame," I say.

Mama's told me that Pigeon and his daddy have it harder than most folks. She says they don't fish just for the love of it. They *need* to fish so they can eat.

In all the time we've been fishing alongside Pigeon and his daddy, we've never said a word to them, and they've never said a word to us. Not a word.

Today's no different. At first, the Troops pretend they don't see us. But when I look in Pigeon's direction, he holds on with his eyes, like he wishes he could speak to me. "Watch the water, Reenie," Mama says, her face getting tight.

Mr. Troop puts a hand on Pigeon's back. "Keep with this side of things," he says, all firm.

That's when Mama tells me how the river got its nickname. "Jim Crow is the law of the land," she explains. "The law that says black people have a place, white people have a place, and the two should steer clear of each other."

"But, Mama," I say, "rivers are for everybody."

Mama tries to help me understand. "That's true in nature's eyes, Reenie. But folks who fish have their own ideas. We and white folks have kept our distance here, for as long as **memory** serves."

Mr. Troop and Pigeon set down their gear on the riverbank, not far from Mama and me. Their voices pierce the dawn.

"Come away from the water, son," Mr. Troop calls. "You'll spook the fish with all that commotion."

"With all the flitting," I say quietly, so only Mama can hear.

Mr. Troop baits his hook with night crawlers. He and Pigeon never catch any fish with those crawlers. Someone needs to tell them that the crawlers are too scrawny this time of year. That carp like corn and bread balls best.

There's a chilly bite to the air. Mr. Troop has got his cap pulled down low over his eyes. Pigeon's singing "Boggle Mo," a ditty that I'd bet a whole dollar makes the carp want to plug their ears.

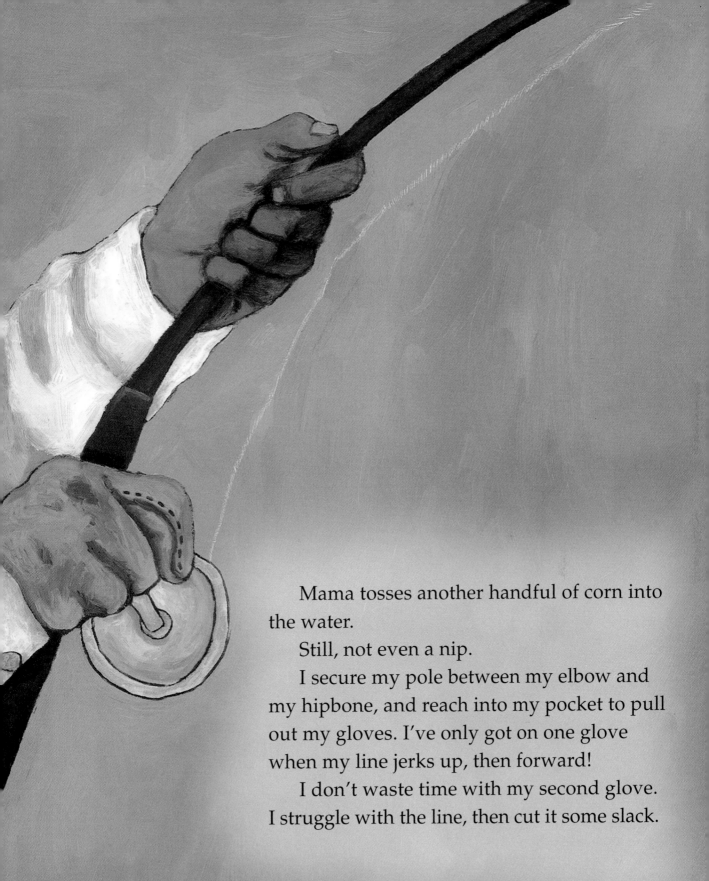

Mama tosses another handful of corn into the water.

Still, not even a nip.

I secure my pole between my elbow and my hipbone, and reach into my pocket to pull out my gloves. I've only got on one glove when my line jerks up, then forward!

I don't waste time with my second glove. I struggle with the line, then cut it some slack.

Finally I reel in the line. Sure enough, I've hooked a nice big carp.

"A keeper," Mama says. "She's beautiful, Reenie! *Beautiful*."

After we've linked our first catch to the carry-chain, Mama's line starts to dance. She's got a feisty one, another keeper. We link her catch with mine, and bait our hooks again. This time I toss the corn kernels, and I can see the carp coming to greet them.

"The news is out that we got corn," Mama says. "The carp are telling all their friends." She laughs.

Pigeon and Mr. Troop haven't caught a thing. When Mr. Troop adjusts the grip on his pole, his reel breaks. He looks like he's trying hard to keep his eyes on fixing his pole, but I see him sneaking glances at Mama and me.

"They always get a catch," I hear Pigeon whine.

"Hush up, boy," Mr. Troop says. "And mind your own business." He stomps off to where he's parked on the other side of a hill. "We just need some pliers from the truck, is all."

Pigeon sets down his pole next to his daddy's and starts sending little stones into the river again. But he's not skipping the stones now—he's flinging them. He blows into his cupped hands to keep them warm. He sniffs hard, like he's trying to hold something in. Then he's back to chucking stones.

But this time he's chucking stones toward Mama and me!

The first one he throws doesn't come close. But the second one nicks me on my knee. I let go of my rod and rub my leg hard. "*Mama*," I wail.

Mama hugs me to her, helping me ease the sting that's charging up in me. "That boy's hurting," she says gently, her jaw firm. "And he can't help but spread his hurt around."

"Let's just go home, Mama," I snap.

Mama shakes her head no. She gathers up our sack of corn and our rods. We go to a place farther down the river. Mama's quiet.

My line tugs for the second time that day. I've got another carp, a long one, its yellow belly glistening under the morning sun. Pigeon's looking straight at us. Even from where we're fishing, I can see he's working hard not to cry. And there's shame on his face. He looks sorry for what he did.

Mama and I carefully string my fish onto the carry-chain with the others, then I reach into our sack for a new corn kernel to bait my hook.

As soon as I feel my hand curl around those nubby kernels, I know what I've got to do.

I gather up the corn sack and start toward Pigeon, sliding Mama a single backward glance. She nods.

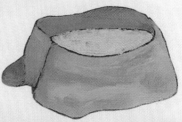

When Pigeon sees me coming with our bag of corn, he looks scared and glad, all at the same time. I can see that his hands are raw from the cold. "My name's Reenie," I say, giving him the glove from my pocket.

"I'm Peter—Peter Troop."
He turns his eyes toward the hill. There's no sign of his daddy.

I pull out a fistful of corn from my sack. "Here," I say, offering the kernels to Peter.

"They'll call up the carp," I tell him. He nods like he already knows. But he won't take the corn.

I bait Peter's hook for him. "Now all you gotta do is wait and *be still*," I say, hoping he'll give his stone throwing a rest.

I leave my small mound of corn on the grass next to Peter and go back to where Mama's still fishing. When I look sidelong down the river, I can see that Peter's **scattering** the corn into the water in front of him. Then he sits with his rod just as patient as can be. He's quiet, too. Quiet and still.

When Mr. Troop comes back, Peter's got a snap-tug on his fishing line. Mr. Troop is all giddy. He rushes to help Peter reel in the line.

Mama gives a single nod. "The corn'll do it every time," she says to me.

"Bring her in easy, now," I whisper, struggling to keep my eyes straight ahead on my own bit of water.

When Peter brings in his line, he's got two fish— one on his hook, the other one biting the first fish's tail! Mr. Troop claps Peter's shoulder. "*My* boy," he says. I can see that Peter's proud.

Soon Peter and his daddy pack up their tackle box and head for their truck. I can't see them drive away, but I hear their truck barreling off.

"I guess Lady Luck's smiled on them," Mama says.

"She's smiled double," I say, feeling a little giggle rise up in me.

The next day Mama and I are walking home from church when I spot the Troops' truck crossing the north bend of the hill, near Jim Crow River. When the truck circles around, it's coming toward Mama and me.

Mr. Troop's got his eyes fixed on the road. I look real hard to see Peter, but he's not in the cab next to his daddy.

Then the truck grunts ahead. I turn to watch it pass, and I see Peter sitting in the flatbed. He's looking right at me and waving with the glove I gave him. And I wave back.

Author's Note

I grew up in the Chemung County region of New York State, where fishing was a favorite pastime. I remember summers when my cousins and uncle collected fishing bait and showed me how to force worms or bread chunks onto a hook to catch fish. It was around this time, when I was seven, that I first began to experience prejudice first-hand, mostly at school. My parents, and the relatives who taught me about fishing, gently began to explain the harsh realities of discrimination.

The separate-sides-of-the-river scenario would play itself out again and again—on the school bus, on the kickball team, in the school cafeteria; where white children stuck together, black children stuck together, and few of us made attempts to mix.

I hated feeling that I was on one side of an invisible fence, and that white children were on the other. Worst of all, I grew to hate my desire to befriend white children whose games and laughter seemed just like mine. And, all the while, I couldn't help but wonder if *they* wanted to be friends with *me*.

I wrote *Fishing Day* to show that children, if given the chance, will often do what is right. *Fishing Day* comes from the belief that generosity and kindness reach beyond all boundaries.

—*Andrea Davis Pinkney*

New Ideas

**THEME
Question**

How can new ideas change our lives and the world around us?

Focus Questions

How do inventions change life?

How do we find solutions?

How can learning something new change our lives?

How might inventions create new challenges?

what a Great Idea!

by Sarah Edwards

Contents

Chapter 1

Make a Discovery!

An idea can come from almost anywhere. Some ideas come from thinking about a problem. Some ideas come from learning new things. Others come from having a flash of inspiration.

Great ideas can lead to great inventions such as making a new device, product, or way of doing things. Inventions can be big or small. Microwave ovens, bicycles, and wind turbines are inventions. So are lightbulbs, can openers, and even chocolate chip cookies! Inventions have helped people to live safer, happier, and better lives.

wind turbine

Often, inventing something means trying out a few different ideas. Imagine you're trying to create a new recipe. You put all kinds of different foods together. Some things taste good together. Others taste terrible! It takes time to invent a new recipe.

Nuts!

George W. Carver was a botanist. He tried something new with peanuts. During the early 1900s he invented more than 300 products from peanuts. He is sometimes called "the father of the peanut industry."

What a Great Idea! 451

Great Mistakes

Some inventions don't begin as ideas at all. Instead, they begin as mistakes! In 1930 Ruth Wakefield ran out of baker's chocolate while she was making chocolate cookies. So she used broken pieces of chocolate instead. She hoped that the chocolate would melt in the oven, but it didn't. Wakefield had accidentally invented chocolate chip cookies!

chocolate

Alexander Fleming

Some very important inventions began as mistakes too. In 1928 the scientist Alexander Fleming was studying bacteria. He forgot to throw away some bacteria before he went on vacation. The bacteria became moldy. Fleming looked closely at it. He saw that there was something in the mold that was killing the bacteria. Fleming had **discovered** penicillin. From that discovery many great medicines that fight infection were later invented.

Next time you make a mistake, don't throw it out and start over again. It might be an invention just waiting to be discovered.

Wiping Out a Problem

Great inventions often come about when someone is trying to solve a problem. In 1903 Mary Anderson was on vacation in New York City. She noticed that when it rained or snowed, streetcar drivers couldn't see out of the windshields. They had to open the windows or get out of the car to wipe off the snow and rain.

Mary Anderson

Anderson decided to make a device that wiped the windshield. It was a swinging arm device with a rubber blade. The driver used a lever inside the car to make the arm swing. This solved the problem of the driver having to get out of the car. By 1916 most vehicles had windshield wipers. Anderson's invention made driving safer.

Chapter 2

Solving Problems

An inventor must solve problems to turn an idea into something real. A good way to find a solution to a problem is to use your problem-solving skills—and your imagination.

Problem-solving Plan

1. *What's the problem?*

2. *How could I solve it?* Brainstorm ideas for solving the problem.

3. *Take action!* Choose an idea and try it.

4. *Did it work?* Check to see if that solution works. Make changes if needed, or try another solution.

The Rainy Day Problem

1. What's the problem?

When it rains during recess, a third-grade class has to stay indoors. They always run out of fun things to do.

2. How could they solve it?

The class brainstorms some activities for rainy days:

- Put on a play and perform it for other students.
- Make a "games corner" with board games, card games, and books.
- Have a fun debate.

3. Take action!

The class decides to hold a debate.

4. Did it work?

The debate is fun, but it's too noisy! It disturbs students who want to read or draw quietly. The class will need to try another idea.

Keep on Trucking

Alvin Lombard was an engineer in the early 1900s. He wanted to invent a vehicle to haul logs. At this time, vehicles with wheels would usually get stuck in the snow. So horses were used to tow logs on sleds from the woods. But horses weren't very easy to steer. They weren't good at pulling heavy loads either.

Lombard thought about how to solve the problem. Instead of using wheels on his vehicles, he used flat steel bands called caterpillar tracks. The tracks helped the log hauler move smoothly over soft snow. Lombard also replaced the horses with a steering wheel and an engine.

A Bright Idea

Thomas Edison was a great inventor too. He invented more than 1,000 devices! In 1879 Edison invented the first practical lightbulb. But he had to do many experiments to find something that gave off a bright light and lasted long enough. When he did finally invent it, Edison said, "We now know a thousand ways not to build a lightbulb."

Thomas Edison

What Is Genius?

Thomas Edison has been described as a genius because of his inventions. One of his most famous quotes is, "Genius is one percent inspiration . . . and ninety-nine percent perspiration." What do you think he meant by this?

Try and Try Again

There's one thing that inventors should NEVER do—give up! For example, Wilbur and Orville Wright worked at a bicycle store in Dayton, Ohio, but their **ambition** was to fly. The brothers built and tested many different flying machines. Many didn't work, and sometimes the brothers felt discouraged. But every time they tested a machine, they learned something new. They worked hard and improved their machines.

In 1903, after four years of work, their machine called the *Flyer* took flight for a few seconds. It was the world's first powered flight.

The Wright brothers had made history! Their ideas are still used in modern aircraft design today.

Wilbur was on the ground, and Orville was at the controls in the first powered flight on December 17, 1903.

Chapter 3

Every Invention Has a Story

Look at all the inventions around you. An invention can be as simple as a button. It can be as complex as a telephone. Inventions can change our lives. They can help us learn new things.

An invention can be a tool or machine, such as a computer. It can be a way of using technology, such as canning foods. Some inventions are useful, such as the pen. Some inventions are fun, such as the yo-yo.

yo-yo

People invent for different reasons. Some people have jobs inventing things. Other people invent things because they have lots of ideas. And some people invent because they observe new things. Doctors observe new problems all the time. They use what they know to fix the problems. For example, Dr. Dianne Croteau invented a special mannequin that makes it easier for people to practice CPR (cardiopulmonary resuscitation).

CPR is a procedure that can save someone's life.

mannequin

Inventions Help People

Inventions in medical science, such as special cameras, help doctors figure out what is wrong with a patient. Other discoveries can help doctors treat or even cure their patients.

In 1988 Dr. Patricia Bath invented a tool to help some blind people see again. It could be used to fix a serious eye problem called cataracts. Before Dr. Bath's invention it was hard and sometimes **risky** to fix cataracts. Dr. Bath's invention made it quicker and safer. She has helped to treat and cure many people, giving them back their sight.

Doctors can use new computer technology to study people's eyes.

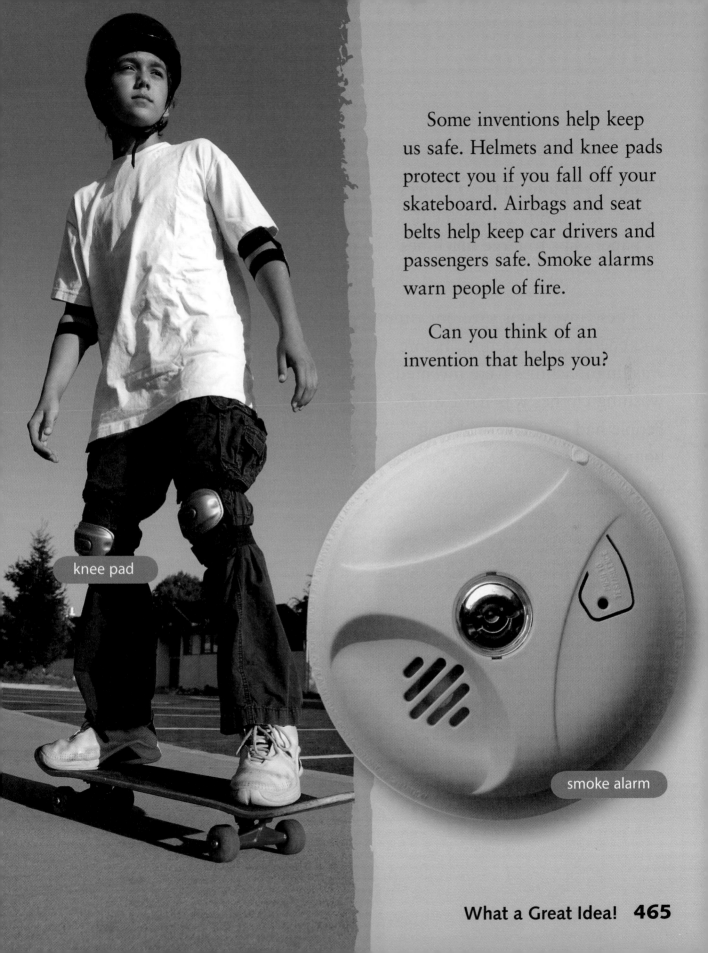

Some inventions help keep us safe. Helmets and knee pads protect you if you fall off your skateboard. Airbags and seat belts help keep car drivers and passengers safe. Smoke alarms warn people of fire.

Can you think of an invention that helps you?

knee pad

smoke alarm

Inventions Make Life Easier and More Fun

Many inventions make our lives easier—from tiny things such as paper clips to large machines such as refrigerators.

These inventions save our time and energy. For example, before washing machines were invented, washing clothes was hard work. People had to use a scrubbing board and a brush. Today we can push a button to wash our clothes. Inventions like these give people time to do other things, such as have fun!

Many inventions change the way people play. MP3 players allow people to carry music anywhere they go. People can also use their MP3 players to listen to educational podcasts.

This invention has led to other inventions too. New clothes and bags have pockets just for MP3 players.

Can you think of an invention that makes your life easier or more fun?

Kids Can Invent

You don't have to be a grown-up to invent something. Krysta Morlan became an inventor in the ninth grade. Krysta has cerebral palsy, and she has had surgery on her legs. For a time she had to wear casts on her hip and ankles. Her skin underneath the casts became itchy and uncomfortable. Krysta had a bright idea. She invented a device with a plastic tube that sends cool air into a cast. Krysta's invention solved her own problem and has helped other people too.

Krysta Morlan

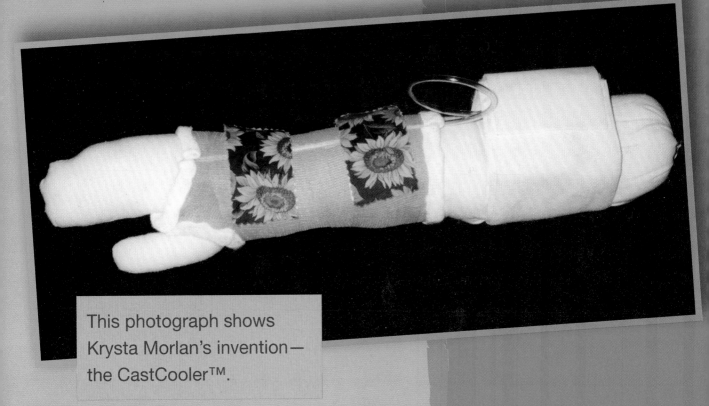

This photograph shows Krysta Morlan's invention— the CastCooler™.

On the Ball

Jacob Dunnack became an inventor when he was only six years old. He'd taken his baseball bat over to his grandma's house to play baseball. But he forgot to bring a ball, so he couldn't play. Jacob came up with a solution. His invention is a baseball bat in which you can store balls.

Jacob Dunnack holds his invention.

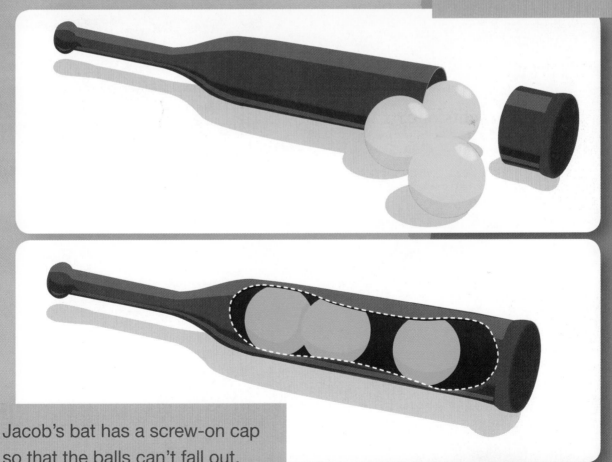

Jacob's bat has a screw-on cap so that the balls can't fall out.

Chapter 4

New Challenges

Some inventions solve one problem only to cause another. When the car was invented, it helped people to move quickly from place to place. However, the car has created some problems. Look at the chart below to compare the **benefits** of cars with the problems they cause.

Benefits	Problems
• The production of cars provides jobs for millions of people. • Cars can transport people and goods quickly. • Cars can give people more freedom to live and work where they want.	• Cars contribute to air pollution. • People may have accidents when they are driving. • People may get less exercise if they always drive a car instead of walking or cycling.

Pollution Solutions

When an invention causes a problem, most inventors see this as a challenge. They need to invent something new that will help solve the problem. For example, people have invented new cars that pollute the air less. A hybrid car runs on electricity as well as gasoline, so it pollutes less than other kinds of cars.

a hybrid car

Who's in Charge?

The invention of the Internet has created challenges. It has opened up a world of information. However, not all of this information is reliable. Any person or group can set up a Web site. They can put any information on it, including false information. They can pretend to be experts about something, even if they aren't. So it's up to people who use the Internet to make sure the information they find is correct.

The Internet has also made it easy for computer viruses to spread. Just like a virus can spread through

your body and make you sick, a computer virus spreads through the Internet and e-mail. Viruses delete or change computer information. But this problem has led to a new kind of business. Inventors have come up with ideas to keep viruses from attacking computers.

Dynamite

Some problems are caused because inventions are used in a way that the inventor didn't intend. The scientist Alfred Nobel invented dynamite. Nobel had intended it to be used for peaceful purposes, such as blasting rocks in mines. But dynamite has been used as a weapon.

dynamite

Future Challenges

Often a lightbulb is used as a symbol for an idea. Why? Sometimes it's hard to solve a problem. All kinds of ideas run through your head. Suddenly you see the answer clearly. It's as if a light has been switched on in your head!

You might think that everything has been invented already. But the light is still switching on in people's heads. People are still thinking of new ideas and new inventions. These inventions will keep on changing the world. Like the car and the Internet, some inventions will create challenges too.

jetpack

robot

In the future people might use jetpacks to get around. What rules will we need to make sure people fly safely?

Or maybe people will use robots to help with chores around the home. How will people make sure their robot follows instructions?

Sum It Up

Every invention begins with an idea. It takes hard work and determination to turn that idea into reality. An invention can be big or small. It can be simple or made up of many parts. It can make life easier, safer, or more fun. It can solve a problem or save a person's life. An invention can even change the world! What kind of thing would you like to invent?

Uncle Rain Cloud

by
Tony Johnston

Illustrated by
Fabricio VandenBroeck

"Tío Tomás looks like a black cloud about to rain." That's what Carlos thought when he saw his uncle waiting for him after school. He'd looked grim ever since the family had moved to LA.

"*La única cosa buena de Los Angeles es su nombre,*" he always said. Like being named for angels was LA's one good claim.

He was a total cloud of gloom. "Uncle Rain Cloud," muttered Carlos. "The perfect name for him."

Uncle Tomás looked darkest on shopping day. Like today.

Carlos's parents always left for work before sunrise, what Mamá called "the first braids of light." Tía Sofía used to shop. She was so fussy about it, the family called her *La Jefa*, the boss-lady of the market. But now she was sick. She stayed mostly in bed doing small jobs, like mending, for Mamá. Uncle Tomás and Carlos went shopping instead.

"*Hola, Tío,*" Carlos called.

Uncle Tomás greeted him with a grunt. "*Vámonos.*" His voice sounded stormy. Not real **anxious** to go.

The market was crowded with carts. Like cars jammed up on the freeway. Slowly, Carlos and his uncle inched along. Uncle Tomás didn't read English, so he studied the pictures on cans and stuff.

"*Te ayudo, Tío?*" Carlos asked.

"*No necesito ayuda,*" he snapped. He never needed help.

Uncle Tomás fumed at everything they selected.

"Milk." "Apples." "Eggs." He spat out the few words he knew like chewed fingernails. To him they sounded ugly—like all of "el Blah-Blah," English. But when they passed the tortillas, Uncle Tomás grabbed some and poked the word on the label.

"*Tortillas siempre son tortillas.*"

Carlos thought, "Tortillas always are tortillas—at least *something's* right."

No matter how grouchy by day, at night, like a worn-out storm, Tío Tomás grew a little calm. While Mamá and Papá shared their day's trials, he told Carlos stories of Mexico, tales of the tongue-twister gods, *los dioses trabalenguas*— *Tezcatlipoca*, Smoking Mirror; *Huitzilopochtli*, Left-handed Hummingbird; *Coyolxauhqui*, She with Golden Bells; *Chalchiuhtotolín*, Precious Turkey, also called *Yoalli Ehécatl*, the Wind.

The harder the names, the more Carlos liked to say them. Sometimes he and Uncle Tomás tried to see how fast they could reel them off. Their tongues stumbled. Bumblers in the dark. They laughed when they got **jumbled** up.

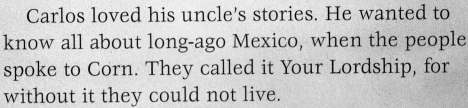

Carlos loved his uncle's stories. He wanted to know all about long-ago Mexico, when the people spoke to Corn. They called it Your Lordship, for without it they could not live.

In the market, when he passed the corn, Carlos said, "Hi, Your Lordship." And he bowed.

When it was time for Carlos's teacher conference, his parents could not go. To gain strength, Tía Sofía must still rest a lot. So who went? Tío Tomás.

For pride, he insisted they bring a gift.

"*Una manzana. Muy gringo,*" he grumped, plunking the apple down like a red rock. Carlos could almost see Tío's anger, perched darkly on his shoulder. Uncle Tomás might wish to be polite, but his weak English made him flare.

"Hello," the teacher greeted them, unflustered.

Uncle Tomás muttered something, but it wasn't "hello." Storm alert—again.

"Please, Uncle Rain Cloud," Carlos said inside himself, "don't get all mad at English now." He prayed to be invisible. Like a little green *gusano* coiled inside an apple. No luck. Still there, about as hidden as his chair.

"I'm very pleased with Carlos's work," his teacher said.

"My uncle doesn't speak English," Carlos whispered miserably.

He knew Uncle Tomás would really blow at that. And he did. Like a silent hurricane, he glared at all things in his path, as if he hoped to flatten them with anger—the chalkboard, the desks, and, of course, those *malditos* books, all in English.

"Then you translate for us." The teacher smiled at Carlos.

She asked Uncle Tomás questions. Gripping his chair, Carlos explained. Back and forth. Forth and back the words lurched. Like a thirsty man lugging well water.

Once the teacher joked, "Are you telling your uncle *everything* I say about your work?"

"Almost everything."

Carlos and his teacher laughed. Uncle Rain Cloud scowled.

Later he grilled Carlos about what she'd said.

"*Qué chistoso*," said his uncle sourly. To him, nothing was funny.

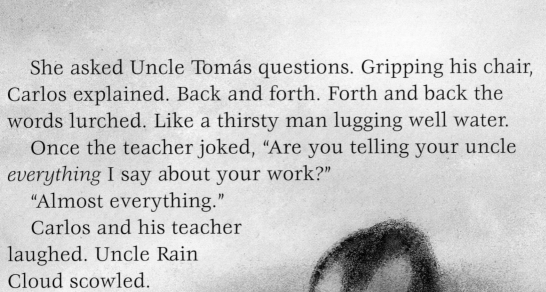

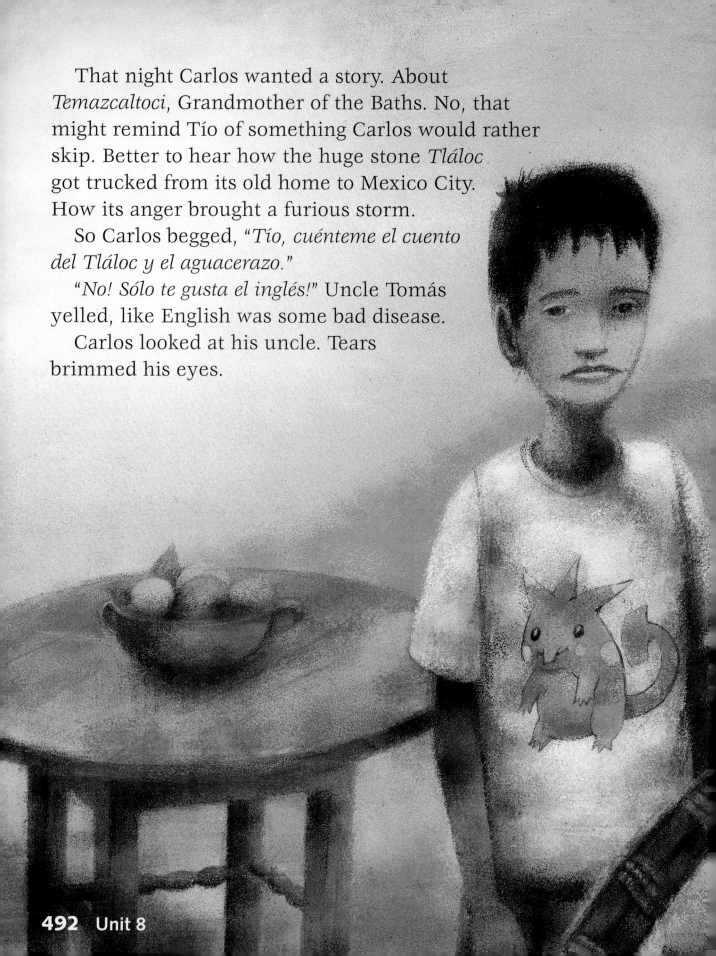

That night Carlos wanted a story. About *Temazcaltoci*, Grandmother of the Baths. No, that might remind Tío of something Carlos would rather skip. Better to hear how the huge stone *Tláloc* got trucked from its old home to Mexico City. How its anger brought a furious storm.

So Carlos begged, "*Tío, cuénteme el cuento del Tláloc y el aguacerazo.*"

"*No! Sólo te gusta el inglés!*" Uncle Tomás yelled, like English was some bad disease.

Carlos looked at his uncle. Tears brimmed his eyes.

It was quiet a long time. Then Uncle Tomás began fumbling. Gently. In Spanish. Carefully, he placed his fingertips together, forming a ball of air, as if that helped him put his words together.

"Carlitos . . . forgive me. These days I am not myself. My *maldito* pride—I feel like a broken-winged bird. A thing that just flops around. You speak for me, a grown man, because—" he said, opening his big hands once more, "because I am . . . afraid to speak English."

Carlos sat stunned. A man and a boy, feeling the same! How could that be?

"It's like that with me, too," he said slowly. "Every day at school, I'm a little afraid. Sometimes it's rough. Kids tease me about my 'lousy Eeengleesh.' But I must go, I must speak. And now I've got friends. I can do stuff. English is pretty OK."

Uncle Tomás put an arm around Carlos. He sat silent, then at last said, "One finds courage in many places. Even in the third grade."

In bed, Carlos closed his eyes
and listened deeply to the night.
Once he thought he heard
something—something flapping . . .

Shopping days were good after that. When Uncle
Tomás and Carlos poked up and down the market
aisles, Carlos pointed to things and named them.
Tío Tomás said them back, stretching the words out
clear to Mexico.

"Potato."

"Po-taaaaay-to."

"Cheese."

"Cheeeeese."

"Green beans."

"Greeeeen beeeeeans."

Whenever they passed the corn, they said,
"Hi, Your Lordship," and both bowed low.
If other shoppers stared, they got
the same treatment—booming
"Hi's" and sweeping bows
to the floor.

One evening when they lugged their groceries inside, Mamá and Papá still weren't home. Another quiet night. Quiet except for Tía Sofía's snoring.

"Would you listen to that woman rumble!" exclaimed Uncle Tomás. "Like she was a big thunder swarm!" Then he told Carlos another rain-god tale, grumbling deep Sofía-rumbles for effect.

All that storm talk reminded Carlos of something.

"Know what I called you when you were always grouchy?"

"What does this 'groochy' mean?" Uncle Tomás asked, all innocent as milk.

"*Enojón,*" Carlos said. "You looked like a cloud about to burst, so I called you Uncle Rain Cloud."

"You had someone else stuck in your mixed-up mind." His uncle chuckled. "*Siempre* I have been Señor Sweet-and-Kind." Then he added, "What is it you name me *now*?"

"I'm still deciding."

Uncle Tomás grinned. "No problem. Call me Your Lordship," he suggested. "Just like Mr. Corn."

They hugged each other hard, and they could feel each other laughing.

Then Uncle Tomás slipped back into Spanish, as he did for important things.

"You have taught me much English, Carlitos. I no longer feel like a broken bird." He flapped his bony elbows like awkward wings. "We will make a deal. You keep teaching me 'el Blah-Blah,' and I will keep teaching you tales of your ancestors—and of all the tongue-twister gods. *In Spanish*."

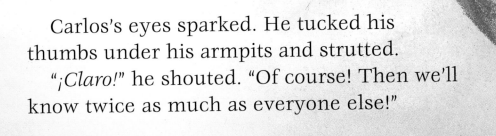

Carlos's eyes sparked. He tucked his
thumbs under his armpits and strutted.

"¡*Claro!*" he shouted. "Of course! Then we'll
know twice as much as everyone else!"

Comprehension Strategy Handbook

How will this handbook help me?

Each page of this handbook will help you choose and use comprehension strategies while you read. Comprehension strategies are tools you can use to help you understand what you read:

Ask and Answer Questions
Determine Important Information
Make Connections
Make Inferences

Make Predictions
Monitor Comprehension
Summarize
Visualize

How do I use the handbook?

The box at the top of each page will remind you what each strategy is and help you decide if you want to use it.

The steps will remind you exactly what you need to do.

The tip will show you a way to keep track of information as you read.

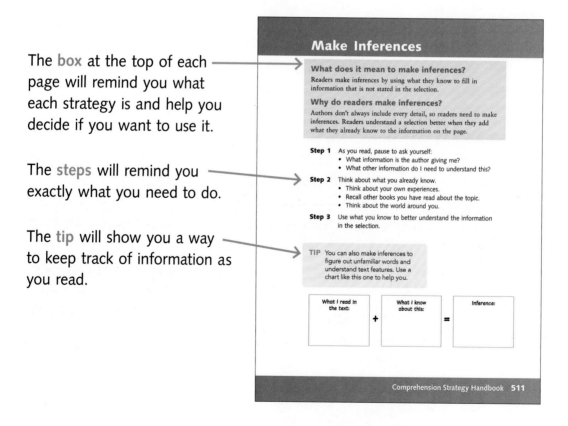

Make Inferences

What does it mean to make inferences?
Readers make inferences by using what they know to fill in information that is not stated in the selection.

Why do readers make inferences?
Authors don't always include every detail, so readers need to make inferences. Readers understand a selection better when they add what they already know to the information on the page.

Step 1 As you read, pause to ask yourself:
- What information is the author giving me?
- What other information do I need to understand this?

Step 2 Think about what you already know.
- Think about your own experiences.
- Recall other books you have read about the topic.
- Think about the world around you.

Step 3 Use what you know to better understand the information in the selection.

TIP You can also make inferences to figure out unfamiliar words and understand text features. Use a chart like this one to help you.

What I read in the text:		What I know about this:		Inference:
	+		=	

Comprehension Strategy Handbook **511**

Can I use multiple strategies?

Yes! Experienced readers use more than one strategy at a time. Read this paragraph to see how each strategy helps you notice and understand different things.

Rani pushed the door open slowly. **Creeaaak!** She peered down the stairs into the pitch-black basement. *Should I really be doing this?* She swallowed hard.

"He-hello?" she called timidly.

There was no answer. Then she heard it again! *What was that noise?* It sounded almost like a giggle.

Rani crept quietly down the stairs. She felt for each step in front of her, counting as she went. One, two, three, four . . . finally her foot hit the last step. She reached for the light switch, but something grabbed her arm! She squeezed her eyes shut and began to scream when all of a sudden—

"Surprise! Happy birthday to you . . . ," her friends began to sing.

Visualize I can really picture this scene in my mind. It gives me the chills!

Make Predictions I've read stories like this before! I think that giggle means her friend is hiding down there.

Make Connections Wow, is she brave! I would never walk into a dark room like that!

Check Predictions Aha! I knew it was going to be her friends!

Ask and Answer Questions

What does it mean to ask and answer questions?

Readers ask themselves questions before, during, and after reading. Sometimes there are questions someone else asks at the end of a selection. Readers find answers in the selection, from their own experiences, or both!

Why do readers ask and answer questions?

Asking and answering questions helps readers check their understanding. It helps them think more deeply about the selection so they better understand it.

Step 1 **Before You Read** As you preview the selection, ask questions to activate prior knowledge and set purposes for reading. For example,
- What is this selection going to be about?
- What do I already know about this topic?
- Is this picture going to be important?

Step 2 **As You Read** Continue asking questions about things you don't understand or things you'd like to find out more about. Keep reading to look for answers to your questions.

Step 3 **After You Read** Are there any questions you have not yet answered? Is there anything new you wonder about now that you have finished reading?

TIP Keep track of your questions in a chart like this one. When you find the answer, write it down! If you don't find the answer, write down other places you could look for it.

Questions	Did you find the answer?		
	Yes	No	Need more information
	✔		

Determine Important Information

What does it mean to determine important information?

Fiction and nonfiction selections include many details that make the writing interesting. But the most interesting ideas may not always be the most important. Determining important information means figuring out the big ideas in the selection.

Why do readers determine important information?

Separating the big ideas from the details helps readers understand the important information the author wants them to know.

Step 1 Look for key words. Key words may be
- in the title, chapter names, and subheads;
- boldface or highlighted;
- repeated in many parts of the selection.

Step 2 Look at the text features. They could be clues about the important ideas in that chapter.

Step 3 Carefully read the first and last sentences in each paragraph. Authors often put important information here.

Step 4 Stop after each section and ask questions.
- What is the most important idea of this section?
- Can I pick out a sentence that tells the most important idea?
- Which information is interesting but not that important?

TIP Use a chart to help you determine important information as you read. Write the big ideas in the left column. Write the supporting details in the right column.

Big Ideas	Supporting Details

Make Connections

What does it mean to make connections?

Readers make connections when something they read reminds them of other things they know. Readers make connections to their own experiences, to other things they have read, and to what they know about the world around them.

Why do readers make connections?

Readers understand a selection better when they can find ways to connect it to things they already know.

Step 1 Before you read, preview the selection and look for words, pictures, or ideas that are familiar to you. Ask yourself:
- What do I already know about this topic?
- What else have I read about this topic?

Step 2 When you read a part of the selection that reminds you of something, stop and jot it down.
- **Text-to-Self** Does it remind you of your own experiences?
- **Text-to-Text** Does it remind you of something else you have read?
- **Text-to-World** Does it remind you of something you know about the world?

Step 3 Think about how the connection you made helps you better understand the selection.

TIP Use sticky notes to record connections you make! Label them like this:
S = self
T = other texts you've read
W = the world

T: I read an article online about this! It also talked about how

S: This character reminds me of m[y] friend Brian. The[y] both get into tro[uble] but they mean w[ell]

W: I don't think the character understands that it's hard for everyone to make friends sometimes.

Make Inferences

What does it mean to make inferences?

Readers make inferences by using what they know to fill in information that is not stated in the selection.

Why do readers make inferences?

Authors don't always include every detail, so readers need to make inferences. Readers understand a selection better when they add what they already know to the information on the page.

Step 1 As you read, pause to ask yourself:
- What information is the author giving me?
- What other information do I need to understand this?

Step 2 Think about what you already know.
- Think about your own experiences.
- Recall other books you have read about the topic.
- Think about the world around you.

Step 3 Use what you know to better understand the information in the selection.

TIP You can also make inferences to figure out unfamiliar words and understand text features. Use a chart like this one to help you.

Make Predictions

What does it mean to make predictions?

Making predictions means making informed guesses about what you are reading. If you're reading fiction, think about what might happen next. If you're reading nonfiction, think about the kinds of information you might learn.

Why do readers make predictions?

Readers make predictions to get ready to read and to check their understanding while they read.

Step 1   Before you read, preview the selection by looking at
- the title, chapter names, and subheads;
- illustrations, photos, captions, and other text features.
- Think about whether any words or pictures look familiar.

Step 2   As you read, use clues from the selection and things you already know to make predictions. For example:
- I think what might happen next is . . . because . . .
- I think I'll find out that . . . because . . .

Step 3   Stop once in a while to check your predictions.
- The selection **confirms** my prediction about . . . because it says . . .
- I need to **revise** my prediction about . . . because I found out that . . .

TIP   Use a chart like this one to help keep track of your predictions!

My Predictions	What Actually Happened	My Revised Predictions

Monitor Comprehension

What does it mean to monitor comprehension?

Experienced readers pay attention not only to *what* they read, but also *how* they read. They recognize when they don't understand something. When their comprehension is breaking down, they use fix-up strategies.

Why do readers monitor comprehension?

At some point, all readers have trouble understanding something they read. Monitoring comprehension helps readers notice when they don't understand something and figure out how to fix it.

Step 1   Pause and ask yourself: Do I understand? Try to summarize what you just read. If you can summarize it, keep reading.

Step 2   If you are not sure you understand, use a fix-up strategy.
- **Reread** the section.
- **Keep reading** to see if the author explains further.
- **Slow down** so you don't miss important information.
- **Speed up**—reading one word at a time makes it difficult to put ideas together.
- **Use the images** to see if they *show* what the text *says*.
- **Seek help.** Use a dictionary. Ask someone to help you.

Step 3   Ask yourself again: Do I understand? If not, try another fix-up strategy.

TIP   Follow the arrows to help you decide what to do when you get stuck!

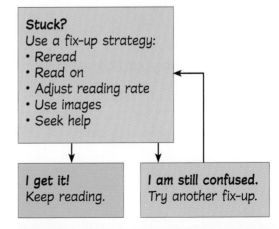

Stuck?
Use a fix-up strategy:
• Reread
• Read on
• Adjust reading rate
• Use images
• Seek help

I get it!
Keep reading.

I am still confused.
Try another fix-up.

Summarize

What does it mean to summarize?

Summarizing means using your own words to explain the most important ideas of a selection you have read. A summary of a nonfiction text tells the most important information. A summary of a story tells who the main characters were and what happened to them.

Why do readers summarize?

Readers summarize to check their understanding and to help them remember what they have read. Readers might stop as they read to summarize part of the text. They might also summarize the entire text once they have finished reading.

Step 1   When you finish a paragraph, chapter, or selection, stop and think about the most important ideas. Make a list.

Step 2   Look over the list and cross out details that are interesting but not that important.

Step 3   Think of a topic sentence that tells the main idea. Ask yourself: What is this text mostly about?

Step 4   Use your list to write sentences that explain the big ideas.

TIP   Use a chart like this one to decide which information to include in your summary.

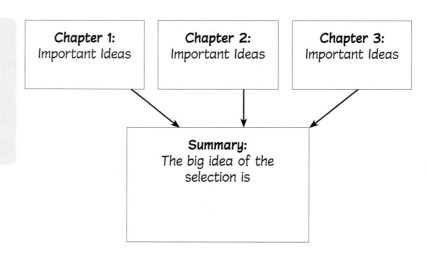

| Chapter 1: Important Ideas | Chapter 2: Important Ideas | Chapter 3: Important Ideas |

Summary:
The big idea of the selection is

Visualize

What does it mean to visualize?

When readers visualize, they use the words on the page to create pictures in their minds. Readers picture the people, places, and things the author describes.

Why do readers visualize?

Visualizing helps readers see, feel, and hear what the author describes. When readers visualize, they can imagine being a part of the story.

Step 1 Look for clues in the selection that signal it might be a good time to visualize:
- Descriptive words
- Actions
- Comparisons

Step 2 Think about your own experiences. Use the selection and your own ideas to create a picture in your mind.

Step 3 As you read on, use new information from the selection to add to or revise your mental picture.

TIP You can draw pictures to help you visualize!

Words from the Selection	The Picture in My Mind

Strategies at a Glance

Use this chart to help you decide which strategies to use.

Ask and Answer Questions Do you find yourself wondering about something you read? Asking and answering questions helps build understanding.
Determine Important Information Which ideas are important, and which ones are supporting details? Figuring out what is important will help you better understand the selection.
Make Connections Does something you read remind you of your own experiences? Does it remind you of something else you have read or something in the world?
Make Inferences Did the author leave out some information? Sometimes readers need to "fill in the blanks" by using what they already know. Making inferences helps you make sense of what you read.
Make Predictions Are you wondering what is going to happen next? Make a prediction and then check it as you read.
Monitor Comprehension Not sure you understand something? Stop and check your understanding. Then try using a fix-up strategy, such as rereading, using images, or reading on.
Summarize Can you sum up what you just read using your own words? Try summarizing to help you remember what you have read.
Visualize Is the author using descriptive words or figurative language? Use the words to make a picture in your mind.

Glossary

adaptation (ad′ ap tā′ shən) *n.* a feature or way of behaving that helps a living thing to survive in its habitat;

Living in groups is an adaptation that helps meerkats keep safe from predators. **330**

affect (ə fekt′) *v.* to cause a difference to something or someone;

Bears affect many animals in the forest. **344**

amazing (ə māz′ ing) *adj.* great or wonderful;

Winning the soccer game was amazing! **279**

ambition (am bish′ ən) *n.* the drive to achieve;

His ambition was to score 40 points in a single game. **460**

ancient (ān′ shənt) *adj.* of or relating to a very long time ago;

The archaeologist found an ancient fossil. **215**

anxious (angk′ shəs) *adj.* uneasy or worried;

He was anxious to get there on time. **480**

approach (ə prōch′) *v.* to move closer;

She didn't want to approach the growling dog. **297**

believe (bi lēv′) *v.* to feel sure that something is true;

People believe that things will get better. **394**

benefit (ben′ ə fit) *n.* a good outcome;

The benefit of riding a bicycle was that she saved on bus fares. **470**

business
(biz′ nis) *n.* an activity that some people do to make a living;
She started a business selling flowers. **148**

carry (kair′ ē) *v.* to move someone or something around;
She decided to carry the baby to the park. **355**

challenge (chal′ enj) *n.* a difficult job or test;
Doing the math problem was a challenge. **272**

choose (chōōz) *v.* to decide;
He had to choose which way to go. **10**

classify (klas′ ə fī) *v.* to arrange things by how they are similar;
He sat down to classify his model car collection. **91**

clue (klōō) *n.* a fact that gives an idea about something that is not fully known;
The movie ticket gave a clue about where she was on Saturday night. **231**

community (kə myōō′ ni tē) *n.* a group of people living together in one place;
She supported her community by helping clean up the park. **139**

compete (kəm pēt′) *v.* to struggle against other living things to survive;
Birds and mammals compete for water in the desert. **338**

confused (kən fyōōzd′) *adj.* unsure of what to do;
She was confused about where to go. **22**

decision (di sizh′ ən) *n.* a choice you have made;
They made a decision about which path to take. **25**

discover
(di skuv′ ər) *v.* to find out or see for the first time;
Alexander Fleming was the first person to discover penicillin. **453**

disturb (di stərb′) *v.* to unsettle;
She had a lot to do, so she asked that no one disturb her. **292**

electricity (i lek tris′ i tē) *n.* a kind of power that makes machines and tools work;
We use electricity to run TVs, computers, and many other machines. **98**

energy (en′ ər jē) *n.* the ability to do work;

The cyclist uses energy to ride a bike. **78**

enormous (i nôr′ məs) *adj.* very big;

They lived in an enormous house with twelve rooms. **229**

environment (en vī′ rən mənt) *n.* the surroundings or conditions in which a person, animal, or plant lives;

The smoke and waste from the factory had a big effect on the environment. **218**

familiar (fə mil′ yər) *adj.* well-known;

He had lived there all his life, so the streets were very familiar. **41**

famous (fā′ məs) *adj.* known by many people;

Christopher Reeve was a famous actor. **283**

food chain (fō̄d chān) *n.* a series of animals and/or plants that depend on one another for food;

The grass, the deer, and the wolves were all part of a food chain. **349**

force (fôrs) *n.* a push or pull;

She hit the ball with as much force as she could. **76**

fossil (fos′ əl) *n.* the remains of an animal or plant that lived long ago;

He found a fossil of a dinosaur in the rock. **206**

freedom (frē′ dəm) *n.* the ability to make choices;

They had the freedom to say what they thought. **389**

geography (jē og′ rə fē) *n.* the study of Earth, its people, and its natural features;

He studied geography to find out about his country. **138**

habitat (hab′ i tat) *n.* the place where one kind of plant or animal can live;

The frog's habitat was the pond. **325**

inspiration (in spə rā′ shən) *n.* a sudden and exciting idea;

She came up with the idea in a moment of inspiration. **450**

jumble (jum′ bəl) *v.* to mix up;

He decided to jumble up the pieces of the jigsaw puzzle. **485**

layer (lā′ ər) *n.* a level of material that covers another level;

He wore a thick layer of wool to keep warm. **200**

memory (mem′ ə rē) *n.* a thought about the past;

For an adult, she had a good memory of her childhood. **425**

migrate (mī′ grāt′) *v.* to move from one place to another;

Some birds migrate to where it is warmer. **335**

observe (əb zûrv′) *v.* to look closely;

She moved closer to observe the ants' nest. **91**

ordinary (ôr′ dn er ē) *adj.* usual, normal;

It was an ordinary cake without fancy frosting. **400**

organize (ôr′ gə nīz′) *v.* to arrange things in a way to get things done;

It took weeks to organize the school dance. **405**

owe (ō) *v.* to have to pay;

They owe the man five dollars for the tickets. **185**

prepared (pri paird′) *adj.* ready;

She was prepared with extra water for the long hike. **53**

provide (prə vīd′) *v.* to supply;

He had to provide his guest with breakfast. **290**

responsibility (ri spon′ sə bil′ i tē) *n.* a duty;

She had the responsibility of doing her homework. **12**

right (rīt) *n.* something a person is not denied;

He had the right to vote in the election. **389**

risky (ris′ kē) *adj.* full of danger;

It was risky to climb the mountain without safety equipment. **464**

scatter (skat′ ər) *v.* to throw things in different directions;

Mom began to scatter the grass seeds over the earth. **438**

search (sûrch) *v.* to look for;

She had to search the whole house to find her bag. **110**

shadow (shad′ ō) *n.* the dark shape formed when an object blocks light;

The sun had almost set so we could see the shadows of the trees. **108**

skill (skil) *n.* talent based on training or experience;

She had great skill as a tennis coach. **35**

technology (tek nol′ ə jē) *n.* special tools and machines that make jobs easier; or the use of skills and knowledge to make tools, machines, or materials;

They used the best technology for building the house. **82**

terrible (tair′ ə bəl) *adj.* very bad;

The movie was terrible, so Yuki left before it finished. **271**

tough (tuf) *adj.* strong;

The rope was tough and would not break. **269**

tourist (tŏŏr′ ist) *n.* a person who visits another place for enjoyment;

She wanted to be a tourist and visit San Francisco. **155**

trade (trād) *v.* to buy and sell goods with other countries;

The United States began to trade with China. **161**

travel (trav′ əl) *v.* to go from place to place;

I travel to school each day by bike. **353**

trickle (trik′ əl) *v.* to flow in drops;

The rain began to trickle through the hole in the roof. **211**

village (vil′ ij) *n.* a very small town;

The village had only one store. **158**

volunteer (vol ən tîr′) *n.* a person who does a job or helps out without pay;

He was a volunteer and helped out at the shelter. **401**

wealth (welth) *n.* a large amount of money or resources;

He gave all his wealth to charity. **166**

Index

Acknowledgments

Photo Credits:

6 (l) ©Kablonk!/Photolibrary; (r) ©stockbyte/Getty Images; **7** (t) ©Stockxpert/Jupiterimages; (l) ©Monkey Business Images/Photolibrary; (r) ©Stockbyte/Getty Images; **8** (tl) ©Punchstock/ImageSource; (bl) ©©Stockxpert/Jupiterimages; (r) ©Jim Esposito Photography L.L.C/Getty Images; **9** (tl) ©Picturenet/Getty Images; (tr) ©Fancy/Veer/Corbis; **10** ©Diamond Mitch//Photolibrary; **11** ©Jose Luis Pelaez Inc/Photolibrary; **12** (t) ©Corbis/Photolibrary; (b) ©Ryan McVay/Photolibrary; **13** ©Tetra Images/Photolibrary; **14** ©Yellow Dog Productions/Getty images; **15** ©Stockxpert/Jupiterimages; **16** (t) ©FOTOG/Getty images; (b) ©Stockxpert/Jupiterimages; **17** ©Ryan McVay/Getty Images; **18** ©Creatas/Photolibrary; **19** (t) ©Photos.com/Jupiterimages; (b)(bgrnd) ©Stockxpert/Jupiterimages; (b)(fgrnd) ©Stockxpert/Jupiterimages; **20** (t) ©Stockxpert/Jupiterimages; (b) ©Monkey Business Images/Photolibrary; **21** ©Kablonk!/Photolibrary; **22** (t) ©ImageSource/Getty Images; (b) ©Nicholas Prior/Getty Images; **23** ©Robert Warren/Getty Images; **24** ©Stephen Simpson/Getty Images; **25** (t) ©Ingram Publishing/Getty Images; (b) ©Pixland/Jupiterimages; **26** (t) ©Jacques Loic/Photolibrary; (b) ©Larry Bones/Photolibrary; **27** © Lilly Dong/Getty Images; **28** (t) (bgrnd) ©Andrew Olney/Getty Images; (t)(fgrnd) ©Stockxpert/Jupiterimages; (b) ©Stockxpert/Jupiterimages; **29** ©stockbyte/Getty Images; **30** ©Jose Luis Pelaez Inc/Getty Images; **31** (t) ©Karin Dreyer/Getty Images; (b) ©Stockxpert/Jupiterimages; **32** (b) ©Mary Kate Denny/PhotoEdit; **33** (t) ©Katsutoshi Hatsuzawa/NEOVISION/Getty Images; (b) ©Yellow Dog Productions/Getty Images; **34** (t) ©Stockxpert/Jupiterimages; (b) ©Comstock Images/Jupiterimages; **35** ©Stockbyte/Getty Images; **36** ©Stockxpert/Jupiterimages. **72** (bl) ©David Young-Wolff/PhotoEdit; (br) ©Ton Koene/Alamy; **73** (t) ©SW Productions/Brand X/Corbis; (bl) ©Image Source/Getty Images; (br) ©Shenval/Alamy Images; **74** ©blue jean images/Getty Images; **75** (l) ©Dana White/PhotoEdit; (r) ©SW Productions/Brand X Pictures/Getty Images; **76** ©Andersen Ross/Getty Images; **77** (t) ©David Young-Wolff/PhotoEdit; (b) ©Brand X Pictures/Jupiterimages; **78** ©Stockxpert/Jupiterimages; **79** (t) ©Thinkstock Images/Jupiterimages; (b) ©Index Stock Imagery/photolibrary; **80** ©Sean Justice/Getty Images; **81** (b) ©Thomas Northcut/Getty Images; **82** ©Creatas Images; **83** (t) ©Retrofile/Getty Images; (b) ©Bettmann/Corbis; **84** (t) ©Brand X Pictures/Punchstock; (b) ©J. R. EYERMAN/Getty Images; **85** (t) ©INTERFOTO Pressebildagentur/Alamy; (b) ©Lambert/Getty Images; **86** (t) ©Ton Koene/Alamy; (bc) ©Brand X Pictures/Punchstock; (bl) ©Bettmann/Corbis; (br) ©INTERFOTO Pressebildagentur/Alamy; **87** (t) ©Todd

Wright/Getty Images; (bl) ©Getty Images; (bc) ©The McGraw-Hill Companies Inc./Ken Cavanagh Photographer; (br) ©High Threlfall/Alamy; **88** (t) ©AFP/Getty Images; (b) ©Greg Baker/AP Images; **89** ©Jonathan Nourok/Getty Images; **90** (t) ©Photos.com/Jupiterimages; (b) ©Image Source/Getty Images; **91** (t) ©Stockxpert/Jupiterimages; (bl) ©Richard Wear/Design Pics/Corbis; (br) ©Ingram Publishing/Age Fotostock; **92** (t) ©Andy Sotiriou/Getty Images; (bl) ©Siede Preis/Getty Images; (br) ©Siede Preis/Getty Images; **93** (tl) ©IT Stock Free/Alamy; (tr) ©Peter Cade/Getty Images; (bl) ©Ingram Publishing/Alamy; (br) ©IT Stock Free/Alamy; **94** (t) ©amana images inc./Alamy; **95** (t) ©NASA JPL; **96** ©Photodisc Collection/Getty Images; **97** ©ImageDJ/Alamy; **98** ©Getty Images; **99** ©Jose Carillo/PhotoEdit; **100–101** ©Shenval/Alamy Images; **101** ©Royalty-Free/Corbis; **102** ©Steve Cole/Getty Images. (bgrnd) **thru-out** ©Brandon Laufenberg/istockphoto/Getty Images; **134** (l) ©Ken Gillham/photolibrary; (r) ©Sylvain Grandadam/Getty Images; **135** (t) ©TongRo Image Stock/Alamy; (bl) ©Kevin Fleming/Corbis; (b) ©Glowimages/Getty Images; **136** ©Robert Everts/Getty Images; **138** ©Ken Gillham/photolibrary; **139** ©Scenics of America/PhotoLink/Getty Images; **140** ©Michael Robinson/Beateworks/Corbis; **141** ©Tyler Stableford Photography/Getty Images; **142** ©Jeffrey Greenberg/Photo Researchers, Inc.; **143** ©Sylvain Grandadam/Getty Images; **144** ©DLILLC/Corbis; **145** (t) ©TongRo Image Stock/Alamy; (b) ©Yadid Levy/Getty Images; **146** ©Philip Gould/Corbis; **147** (t) ©The Granger Collection, New York; (b) ©Jason Brindel Landscapes/Alamy; **148** ©Kevin Fleming/Corbis; **149** (tl) ©Greg Smith/Corbis; **150** (t) ©Jeff Greenberg/Alamy; (b) ©Doug Menuez/Getty Images; **151** (t) ©Morton Beebe/Corbis; (b) ©Brand X Pictures; **152** ©Atlantide Phototravel/Corbis; **153** ©Royalty-Free/Corbis; **154** ©The Granger Collection, New York; **155** ©Ellen Rooney/Robert Harding World Imagery/Corbis; **156** ©Getty Images; **157** ©John Burcham/Getty Images; **158** ©Steve Allen/Getty Images; **159** (t) ©Stockxpert/Jupiterimages; (b) ©Glowimages/Getty Images; **160** ©DEA PICTURE LIBRARY/Getty Images; **162** (t) ©Hisham Ibrahim/Getty Images; (b) ©AFP/Getty Images; **163** ©DreamPictures/Vstock/Getty Images; **164** ©Hill Street Studios/photolibrary. **194** (l) ©Sandra Ivany/Brand X Pictures/Getty Images; **196** (r) ©Edward Van Hoorick/Getty Images; **197** (t) ©Russell Illig/Getty Images; (bl) ©Tom Bean/Corbis; (br) ©Melvyn P. Lawes; Papilio/Corbis; **198** ©Roger Ressmeyer/Corbis; **198-199** (thru-out) ©Brand X Pictures/photolibrary; **200** (b) ©Sandra Ivany/Brand X Pictures/Getty Images; **201** ©Jeff Foott/Getty Images; **203** ©National Geographic/Getty Images; **205** ©James Balog/Getty Images; **206** (t) ©Ira Block/Getty Images; (b) ©Lowell Georgia/Corbis; **207** ©Don Farrall/Getty Images; **208** ©altrendo images/Getty Images; **210** (tr) ©Edward Van Hoorick/Getty Images; (b) ©NASA; **211** ©Stockxpert/Jupiterimages; **212** ©Robert Van Der Hilst/Getty Images;

Acknowledgments